A STRANGER'S KISS

When Tara was forced to beg for a stranger's help, little did she know what she was getting into. For the sake of her ailing secretarial agency though, she decided to take whatever insults Adam Blackmore cared to hand out. It was only when he insisted on taking her with him to Bahrain that she began to worry. Was this relationship still strictly professional? It had to be. For wasn't Adam the father of his previous secretary's child . . . ?

Books by Liz Fielding
in the Linford Romance Library:

HIS LITTLE GIRL
GENTLEMEN PREFER . . .
BRUNETTES
DANGEROUS FLIRTATION
AN IMAGE OF YOU
ELOPING WITH EMMY
A POINT OF PRIDE
INSTANT FIRE

LIZ FIELDING

A STRANGER'S KISS

Complete and Unabridged

LINFORD
Leicester

First published in Great Britain in 1994

First Linford Edition
published 2010

British Library CIP Data

Fielding, Liz.
 A stranger's kiss. - -
 (Linford romance library)
 1. Love stories. 2. Large type books.
 I. Title II. Series
 823.9'14–dc22

 ISBN 978–1–44480–451–5

Published by
F. A. Thorpe (Publishing)
Anstey, Leicestershire

Set by Words & Graphics Ltd.
Anstey, Leicestershire
Printed and bound in Great Britain by
T. J. International Ltd., Padstow, Cornwall

This book is printed on acid-free paper

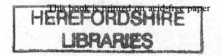

FOR JOHN
MY OWN 'PARFIT GENTIL
KNYGHT'

1

'I don't believe it! Where did he spring from?' Tara Lambert moved quickly to the door but the tail-lights of her partner's car were already disappearing into the blackness of the evening, taking with them any possibility of help from that direction.

She glanced back to where the man was waiting across the street. He too was staring after Beth's car, obviously wondering if Tara had gone home with her partner. Well it was too late to regret refusing the proffered lift, but if she moved quickly it might not be too late to escape.

Shrugging her raincoat collar up high around her ears, she snapped open her umbrella, stepped out into the wet evening and took off swiftly down the street.

She had gone only a couple of

hundred yards when she heard her name being called from the other side of the street. Her escape bid had not, after all, gone unnoticed. With a sinking heart she glanced around her; the shops were already closed and there was nowhere to seek refuge in the shuttered street. Even the taxi rank was deserted, although no cabbie would have thanked her for wasting his time on the short ride to her flat.

She hurried on, urging the traffic lights to stay green and keep the traffic moving, but even as the thought entered her head they flicked to amber.

She stopped, cursing herself for every kind of an idiot. She could have stayed in the office and phoned for a taxi. Maybe it was not too late to beat a strategic retreat.

'Tara!' Her name, much closer, startled her and she glanced back before she could stop herself. He was weaving through the slowing cars and cutting off all possibility of escape in that direction.

A burst of light shone briefly on the pavement just ahead of her and a couple emerged and ran, laughing, their arms about each other, along the road. They had come from the wine-bar on the ground floor of a glossy office development. She had watched it come to life during the past few weeks but a quick glance at the menu outside had convinced her that it was far too pricey to be included on her list of lunch venues. It hadn't surprised her. Everything about Victoria House was expensive. But right now that was the last thing on her mind.

The urgent sound of closing footsteps propelled her through the door before she had time to consider what she would do once inside.

It wasn't quite seven o'clock and it was still busy with people from the surrounding offices and shops, but there was no one she recognised. She dumped her umbrella in a stand and hung up her coat. At least there were plenty of people about, and now she was inside she would have something to eat. It had been a long, hard day and as the aroma of good food assaulted her senses she realised just how hungry she was. She would just have to choose whatever was cheapest on the menu.

As she looked around for a vacant table the door opened behind her. 'Tara!'

Galvanised into movement by the sound of his voice, she threw herself into a bench seat hidden from the door by a small grove of potted palms where a man whose deep concentration on a business document and navy pin-striped suit suggested a certain safety.

'Please pretend that I'm with you!' she whispered, urgently. He looked up, a frown momentarily creasing his wide tanned forehead, and in that instant she knew, without any doubt, that the impression of safety was all illusion.

Despite the touch of silver that streaked across an unruly lock of hair he was younger than she had thought, in his mid-thirties, no more. Not handsome. The word implied a smooth perfection that this man did not possess. His face was rugged. Dark brows jutted fiercely over sea-green eyes that seemed to bore into her, seeking out her inmost secrets. His nose had the unmistakable kink produced by a collision with a rugby boot, or perhaps a fist, his mouth wide and uncompromising above a hard chin. It was the face of a plunderer, a pirate, albeit a twentieth-century one. And his reactions were as swift.

A brief assessing glance over her shoulder was enough. Without hesitation he slipped his arm around her waist and her lips parted on a short, startled breath as he swept her hard against his chest. She caught the faint scent of something clean and masculine. Good soap, leather, something more.

His fingers grazed her cheek and slowly he began to wind a long jet strand of hair that had escaped from restraining pins around his fingers. For a moment she sat, too stunned to move or do anything to stop him. Then, he tucked it behind her ear and while she was still trying to gather her scattered wits he moved swiftly to capture her chin, tilting it upwards, leaving her mouth at his mercy.

'You're late, my darling,' he murmured, his voice a velvet caress. Shaken by this dashing, if unexpected response to her appeal for help, she tried to protest. Then he smiled and the words died in her throat. 'But I forgive you.'

He lied. There was nothing forgiving about the kiss he demanded as a forfeit for his protection. Tara knew the instant his lips claimed hers that this was no 'stage' kiss to fool her pursuer. Whoever this man was, whatever he was, he had never done anything by halves.

For a moment she was stiff, unyielding in his arms, but his expert mouth was not to be denied. Infinitely tender, infinitely assured, he teased her lips apart, exciting a response, a flicker of pleasure that in an instant flamed into desire, and she found herself responding to his unexpected embrace with a warmth that both shocked and elated her.

'Tara!' The petulant voice in her ear had become insistent, recalling her to some semblance of where she was and what she was doing. She had no immediate wish to re-enter the real world, wanting to linger a little while longer wherever it was that his kiss had taken her. She slowly lifted heavy lids that would have much preferred to stay closed. For an endless moment his eyes blazed into hers, holding her as much captive as his arm about her waist. Then his mouth curved in a knowing little smile and Tara gasped and turned away to blot out what she saw in his face. She had enjoyed every moment of that kiss and he knew it. She pushed against the dark cloth of his jacket but made no impression on the hard wall of his chest. It seemed forever before he took pity on her and turned away, directing his attention instead to the man hovering beside them.

'Tara is having dinner with me. If you wish to speak to her you'll have to make an appointment for some other time,' he said. He made his point without any drama. Clearly he was a man who expected to be obeyed without question. Her pursuer blinked and started as if he had only just noticed the other man, so single-minded had been his concentration on his quarry.

'Why don't you come back, Tara?' he demanded. 'You know how much I need you.' His tall, slight figure bundled up in a damp raincoat looked oddly tragic and despite everything Tara felt a touch of guilt as he turned to leave. Then he rounded on her. 'Don't think I'll give up,' he said with unexpected defiance, and she jumped.

The door swung shut and reluctantly, deeply embarrassed by the results of the uncharacteristic impetuosity that had driven her into a stranger's arms, she turned to face him.

'Why did you do that?' she asked, shakily.

'I wasn't quite sure what was expected. But I thought I had better be convincing.' He raised one questioning brow. 'Was I, do you think?'

She ignored the question. He already knew the answer. 'Your presence would have been enough,' she managed.

'Would it?' His eyes were teasing now. 'You should have said.'

'You didn't give me a chance,' she protested, finally regaining control of her vocal cords, if not her hectic pulse.

'I apologise if I didn't meet the required standard as your ' . . . parfit gentil knyght.' It's not a role I've had too much experience in.'

'You're not a knight of any description,' she snapped, then, appalled by her own bad manners, she coloured. 'I'm sorry. I shouldn't have said that. I'm really very grateful for your intervention.'

She knew she should offer an explanation to her deliverer and beat a hasty retreat. Thanks were hardly necessary. He had already claimed his reward, and she was quite certain from the amusement lighting the depths of his eyes that he had derived considerable entertainment at her expense.

But retreat, she found, was not that simple. She tried to move, anxious to effect a dignified withdrawal with all possible speed, but his hand was still about her slender waist, his grip deceptively firm. Tara offered a cool smile and tried again.

'Thank you for your . . . ' she swallowed as his eyebrows rose ' . . . your help,' she finished quickly. 'I'm sorry to have been such a nuisance. It was — '

'There's no need to explain,' he assured her easily. 'It was a pleasure.'

'Yes,' she agreed, then a faint blush coloured her cheeks as she realised what she had said. 'I didn't mean that — '

'Didn't you?' His soft laughter flickered against her like a caress. 'If you meant that the pleasure was all mine, I don't think you're being entirely truthful.' She tore her eyes away from his mesmerising gaze. She had apparently jumped straight out of the frying pan and into the fire. And this time she would have to rescue herself. Her eyes fell on the paper he had been reading and she seized on this, attempting once more to edge free of his grasp.

'You were working and I've disturbed you,' she said, in an effort to distract him.

'Profoundly.' His eyes remained firmly fixed upon her. 'But I have to tell you that I have no complaints.'

She swung to face him, certain now that he was laughing at her. 'I must go.'

'No, Tara. If you go now you'll make a liar out of me,' he objected. 'Not very polite. And your . . . friend might be waiting outside. He seemed very determined to press his suit.'

'I'm sure he'll have gone. He's made his point.'

'It's a regular occurrence, then?' He

11

didn't wait for her answer. 'Perhaps he's your husband?'

The colour drained from her face. 'No.' She shook her head, thankful that Jim Matthews' proposals of marriage did not include anything as romantic as professions of undying love. 'No, he's not my husband.'

'Just some poor lovesick swain.' For a moment pity seemed to touch his eyes. But only for a moment. 'In that case, now I've chased him away you can stay and have dinner with me. I can recommend the pepper steak.'

He ignored her sharp intake of breath at his arrogant assumption that she would accept this peremptory invitation. A glance brought a waitress immediately to their table and he had ordered steaks and salad before she could make any objection. 'You can bring the claret now,' he told the girl.

Once she had gone he unwound his arm from Tara's waist and offered her his hand. 'Perhaps we'd better introduce ourselves, if somewhat belatedly under the circumstances. Adam Black-more. How do you do?' It was a beautiful hand. Large, square, with long square-tipped fingers that she was certain were as experienced in pleasure as his mouth had been.

Tara started, hardly able to believe the direction in which her mind was wandering. Free now, she knew the sensible thing to do was to get up and leave. And she was renowned for her common sense. But the evening had already progressed way beyond sense. His kiss seemed to have driven sense out of the door along with Jim Matthews. She surrendered her hand, trying desperately to ignore the rise in her pulse-rate as he took it and held it firmly in his own.

'How d'you do?' she replied, a little breathlessly. 'Tara Lambert.' Then rebellion lit a tell-tale glint in her warm brown eyes. 'But I think you should know that I'm a vegetarian.'

His grip tightened, his eyes narrowing to take in the strong lines of her face, the drama of dark well-defined brows, a straight no-nonsense nose. He lingered momentarily on the generous curve of her mouth before meeting her wide brown eyes head on. 'No, Tara Lambert. I don't think so.'

She wanted to be angry, but oddly found she couldn't be. 'No,' she admitted, her mouth widening in a smile. 'But I couldn't resist.'

Adam Blackmore's eyes strayed towards the door. 'Perhaps you should try, once in a while, Tara Lambert. Then you wouldn't find yourself in such danger-ous situations.'

'He's not — ' she began, vigorously, but he cut off her words.

'Isn't he?' His look was measuring. 'Who said I was referring to him?' They were interrupted by the arrival of the wine and he poured two glasses. 'Try this. Tell me what you think.'

Tara knew it was ridiculous to feel vexed that he would not listen. She had thrown herself at him somewhat reck-lessly after all, although she hadn't expected her chosen knight errant to be quite so practised in his fielding. Under the circumstances he had every right to assume the worst. So be it. Let him think what he wanted; it really didn't matter. This was one of those isolated moments in time, like a conversation with a stranger in a train. When you reached your destination the acquaintance was at an end. He was simply amusing himself. And she told herself that there was no reason why the fun should be all one way.

With a flick of her wrist, Tara swirled the wine in the glass, then held it for a moment at arm's length so the wine stilled. She brought the glass to her nose and breathed in the spicy fruit-laden scent. She was sorely tempted to sloosh the wine loudly between her teeth, but restrained herself, simply allowing the flavours to fill her mouth.

Adam Blackmore watched this performance with interest. 'Well?' he asked, finally.

Tara demurely lowered her long

15

lashes. 'Mmm. I like it.'

'You like it!' His eyebrows rose a fraction. 'After that performance I expected a trifle more by way of comment.'

'Did you?' she asked, with apparent surprise. She lifted her shoulders in the slightest of shrugs. 'Did you expect me to tell you that this is a 1983 estate-bottled Château Brane Cantenac from the Margaux region?'

He threw back his head and laughed, revealing strong white teeth. 'I should have seen that coming.'

'Perhaps,' she agreed, oddly pleased that he had a sense of humour large enough to laugh at himself. She smiled sweetly. 'Or maybe you should just have anticipated that I am quite capable of reading the label on the bottle. Although I do know enough to appreciate that this isn't house plonk.'

'No, Tara, it certainly isn't that.'

A willowy blonde brought their steaks to the table. 'Just the way you like it, Adam,' she said, and gave Tara an assessing sideways glance. 'Can I get you anything else?'

His smile for the girl was warm. 'Perhaps later.'

Tara watched as the girl walked gracefully back to the kitchen. 'You eat here often?' she asked.

'Now and then,' he affirmed. 'The food is good. I've never seen you in here before.'

'No. I just dived in to avoid . . . ' She stopped self-consciously. 'I had planned to stay and eat though.' She regarded the steak with misgivings. She hadn't planned to eat anything this expensive. Business wasn't exactly booming and money was tight at the moment. But if she was going to pay for it, she might as well enjoy it. She picked up her knife and fork and began to eat.

'Do you work near here?' he asked.

'Just down the road. And you?'

'It's convenient.' There was something in his voice that made her look up, but his face was impassive and he didn't elaborate. 'What do you do?'

Tara considered the question. When two people ran a small business they did everything, including the foot-wearying job of delivering leaflets with details of their secretarial and computer staff agency to all the office blocks in the area during the weekend. But he didn't mean that. 'I'm a secretary,' she said.

'Better than the one who typed this, I hope,' he said, flicking a disdainful finger at the report he had been reading when she interrupted him and which he had pushed out of the way.

'Probably,' she said, non-commitally. But she wasn't about to let an opportunity slip her by. 'If you need secretarial help I could find someone for you.'

'You?' he asked, suddenly quite still. She could almost hear the sound of shutters going up and, instinctively sensing that this was not an appropriate moment for a sales pitch, she let it go.

'No, not me. I have a job.' She changed the subject. 'And you? What do you do?'

He shrugged. 'Nothing very exciting. I sit behind a desk all day, moving figures about.'

Tara looked sideways through her lashes at the figure beside her. She hadn't seen him on his feet but it was clear, even under the civilising business suit, that Adam Blackmore had the lean, hard figure of an athlete. He might spend all day behind a desk, but it raised the question: what did he do with his nights?

Tara felt her cheeks grow warm at the direction her thoughts were taking again. They grew warmer as she realised that he was regarding her with scarcely veiled amusement.

'Yes?' he enquired.

She touched her cheeks self-consciously. 'It's the wine. I'm not used to it.'

'I see.' She had the uncomfortable feeling that he did. All too clearly. 'Are you driving?'

'No. I don't live far.' That had been the urgency behind her wish to shake off Jim Matthews. If he had managed to follow her home he would lay siege to her there as well as the office and there would be no more peace.

Adam refilled her glass. 'In that case, another glass won't hurt.' He ignored her protest. 'The colour in your cheeks is most becoming.'

Glad that her fair skin never managed more than the faintest blush Tara sipped the wine. 'It is very good.'

'Yes. I bought a few cases on a trip to Bordeaux a while back.'

'And you keep it here?' she asked, surprised.

'This was the site of a public house. There are very old cellars that run right under the road.' He eyed her sideways. 'The owner of this place lets me keep all my wine in them.'

Tara nodded. 'The Queen's Head. And I remember them uncovering the cellars during the excavations. But I would have thought the developers would have filled them in.'

'You speak sacrilege, Tara Lambert. Good cellars are hard to find.'

'It's not a subject that crops up in my line of business. But you must know the owner pretty well if you trust him with your personal wine stock,' Tara commented. 'Especially if it's all as good as this.'

Adam Blackmore smiled slightly. 'I suppose you could say we're pretty close.'

The waitress whisked their plates away and Adam asked if she would like a pudding.

Tara shook her head.

'Coffee?'

'No, thank you. That was delicious, but I've eaten far too much already. And I really must go.' He signed the bill, brushing aside her insistence that she pay for her meal, and unwound from the bench. He had seemed dangerous seated, but standing, facing her, she was able to truly appreciate the wide, square shoulders and the fact that he topped her own five feet seven by a good six inches.

He helped her on with her coat, the

touch of his hand on her shoulder sending an unexpected heat through her body. The urgency of it shocked and disturbed her. She moved quickly away, grabbing for her umbrella to cover her agitation. When she turned back he had opened the door for her.

'Thank you, Adam. For everything.'

'Everything? Are you quite sure about that?' He laughed softly at her confusion, then took the hand she had offered and tucked it under his arm. 'I'll walk you home. Just in case your erstwhile pursuer has decided to hang around,' he added, before she could object.

A small stab of disquiet fluttered in her abdomen. 'There's no need. He's not dangerous,' she assured him.

'No. Just a nuisance.' His voice was cool. 'I won't be. Which way?'

'But you haven't a coat,' she objected. It wasn't especially cold for early March. But cold enough. He ignored her objection, simply waiting for her to answer his question. 'It's this way. At least it's stopped raining.'

'So it has and the fresh air is welcome.'

Fresh? She wondered if he indulged in cold showers for fun but didn't voice the thought. The idea of Adam Blackmore in a shower of any sort was far too disturbing. She made an effort to pull herself together.

'After a day behind your desk?' she asked, moderately satisfied with the light bantering tone she achieved.

'After a day behind my desk,' he agreed and then smiled and she knew that he hadn't been fooled for a minute.

'It's along here.' They walked up the side street until they reached the courtyard which had once housed the mews for a great house long since demolished. The stables, coachhouse and quarters above had been converted into small attractive apartments. Tara's first-floor flat had been her home, her refuge, for a little more than six years and as they climbed the steps she wondered, not for the first time, if she had been quite mad to risk it all on a business venture when she could be earning a good salary working for someone else. Someone like Jim. She suppressed a shudder at the thought.

Adam looked around. 'This is unexpected. I thought everything old had long since disappeared in Maybridge.'

'The developers have done their best. But this place was somehow overlooked in the rush to modernise. And fortunately the site wasn't quite big enough for a car park,' she added drily.

Adam held out his hand for her key and after the slightest hesitation she surrendered it. He slid it into the lock and pushed the door open for her. She paused in the entrance and turned to face him. Risk seemed to be in the air. 'Would you like some coffee?' she offered, tentatively.

'You're safely home, Tara. I think perhaps you've taken enough chances for one day.' Heavy lids cloaked the expression in his eyes but his mouth curved into a crooked smile. 'Goodnight.'

He turned and was gone. His feet clattered briskly down the steps and she heard them ringing along the old rain-soaked cobbles of the courtyard before they were finally lost on the softer surface of the main road where they had to compete with the sound of traffic. She closed the door softly, not quite certain if she was glad or sorry that he had gone.

⋆ ⋆ ⋆

It was the sound of her telephone ringing that finally woke her.

'Hello, Tara Lambert,' she mumbled, still half asleep, into the receiver.

'Tara? Are you ill?' Beth Lawrence demanded.

'Ill? No — ' She caught sight of the clock. 'Beth, I'm sorry. I've overslept. I'll be with you in twenty minutes.'

'Thank goodness for that. But don't come to the office. We've had a response to one of those leaflets you delivered at the weekend. You've an appointment at ten-thirty with a Jenny Harmon at Victoria House.' She gave Tara the details and wished her luck.

Tara ducked under a cool shower to finish the job of waking up. She twisted her shoulder-length hair up into a businesslike chignon and then dressed in a well-cut charcoal-grey suit that flattered her tall, slender figure. She checked her document case to make certain she had all the figures she would need and with a final glance in the hall mirror set off briskly to keep her appointment.

The sun was making an effort this morning and the pavements shone as she walked briskly down to the main road, lending an air of promise to the morning. Tara took only the very best secretaries on her agency books for temporary work and a client company that could afford accommodation such as Victoria House would make a big difference to their business. It would have a large clerical staff, all needing holiday and sickness cover. In the twelve months that she and Beth had been running their secretarial and computer staff agency, there was no denying it had been a struggle to break even. This response to her efforts to win new business was just what they needed and it was up to her to make the best of it.

On one side of the ground floor was the wine-bar that had been her refuge of the night before. The reminder of her evening with Adam Blackmore brought a faint blush to her cheeks and a lingering regret that their meeting had been in circumstances that had shown her in such an unfavourable light. She had spent a restless night disturbed by the thought that he might assume she regularly threw herself at strangers in the hope of getting a free meal. She came to an abrupt halt. Maybe he thought she always invited them back to her flat for . . . coffee.

For a moment the brilliant light-filled atrium, with its expensive boutiques, spun giddily. Then she took a deep breath and firmly banished him from her mind. If that was what he thought it was far too late to do anything about it. Certainly too late to withdraw her rash, uncharacteristic invitation. She should just be glad she would never have to face him again.

She stepped quickly on to the escalator and tried to compose herself on the stately ride up to the mezzanine. The receptionist checked her name off a list and told her to take the lift to the twentieth floor where she would be met.

As she was whisked noiselessly upwards she mentally ran over all the things she would say to convince Mrs Harmon that she should give them a chance, determined to make a good impression. The lift came to a halt and the doors slid back.

The figure that filled the space was shadowed, brilliantly backlit by the great floor to ceiling arch of window that faced the entrance to the lift. Then he moved and the light caught the harsh planes of his face bringing it into sharp relief.

'Adam!' Tara's breath left her in a little exclamation of shock as she said his name. The impact made by Adam Blackmore was no less in the clear light of day. Rather the reverse. For a moment they both stood quite still while Tara's confident smile, in place for Jenny Harmon, faded under eyes about as welcoming as the Atlantic on a bad day.

Then the doors of the lift began to slide together, galvanising them both into action, Tara in an attempt to escape before they closed and she was whisked away at the whim of some unseen hand, Adam simply to place a well-shod foot in the way so that they opened again. He stood aside to let her out.

'Tara.' Not a question. No surprise. Her name was simply a statement of some unwelcome, but not unexpected fact.

'Hello, Adam. I didn't expect to see

you here.' Her voice sounded incredibly small and unconvincing even to her own ears. 'You said your office was convenient, but I hadn't realised — '

'No? This is a simple coincidence?' He didn't wait for her reply but gripped her elbow and hauled her across the thickly carpeted hallway.

'Adam!' she protested. 'I have an appointment . . . ' She glanced back, hoping that Jenny Harmon might miraculously appear and explain. There was no one. She needed to get a hold on herself, to calm the hectic pounding of her pulse that his unexpected appearance had accelerated out of control. But he didn't give her the opportunity. He opened one of a handsome pair of doors, propelled her firmly through and deposited her in a chair.

She had a brief impression of being on top of the world, of distant woods and the river framed in a series of arched windows that flooded the room with sunshine. Then he released her and she leapt to her feet. She wasn't in Victoria House to admire the view.

'I have an appointment with Mrs Harmon,' she said, a sudden flash of anger finally releasing her vocal cords. 'Will you please direct me to her office?'

'Sit down, Tara.' He settled himself on the corner of a large uncluttered desk and without taking his eyes from her face he leaned across and punched a button on his intercom. 'Sit down!' he commanded, when she did not immediately obey. She subsided into the chair, certain that he was not above picking her up and dumping her into it. But she perched on the edge, defiant in her determination not to stay a moment longer than she had to.

'Jenny, are you expecting a Tara Lambert this morning?' he asked.

'Yes, Adam. She's from the secretarial agency I was telling you about. She has arrived, but she appears to be lost somewhere in the building.'

'I very much doubt that she's lost.'

31

His mouth curved in a smile Tara didn't much care for. 'In fact I believe she's exactly where she wants to be. Leave it with me.' For a moment he didn't speak. He remained on the corner of his desk, regarding her with every evidence of irritation. Then, as if he had come to some decision, he stood up and settled himself in the chair opposite her.

He rested his elbows on the desk, the tips of his fingers touching his chin as he regarded her thoughtfully. 'Once, Tara,' he said, at last, 'might be considered simple chance. Even an encounter as apparently contrived as the one you arranged last night.' He ignored her furious denial. 'But twice?' Mrs Harmon is on the twentieth floor. This is the twenty-first. My private apartments.'

'Then I must have touched the wrong button.' She stood up. 'A simple mistake, easily remedied. There's no need to disturb yourself any further.'

'Stay where you are!'

'Why? So that you can insult me some more? No, thank you.' She didn't sit, but she did stay where she was. It seemed improbable that there was any chance of business with this company now, but she owed it to Beth and to an increasingly tetchy bank manager to make every effort to redeem what she could from the mess. 'I'm sorry to have disturbed you, Adam. I came here at the invitation of Mrs Harmon to talk to her about temporary secretarial help. I should like to do that now, if I may.'

'You may not. Talk to me. Convince me that you have something worth selling.' His eyes were cold. 'Not quite so easy with your clothes on. But give it your best shot.'

'I beg your pardon?' The words were shocked from her.

'That's what you wanted, surely?' He sat back. 'You threw yourself into my arms last night. Invited me into your flat for what is euphemistically known as a 'cup of coffee'. But unfortunately I didn't take the bait. So now you're here. Sit down, Tara. Make your pitch. Who knows? I might still be tempted.'

2

Tara exploded. 'Just what kind of a girl do you think I am!'

'I'll give you ten minutes to demonstrate.' His eyes coolly assessed the length of her figure. 'The method I leave entirely up to you.'

Tara sat down quickly. She had already rejected any thought of trying to explain. He would simply switch off and the opportunity would be lost forever. If Adam Blackmore was the head of this company she might as well do as he suggested while she had his attention and make her 'pitch'. And there was no time to lose. She immediately launched into an outline of the high quality service offered by her agency before he changed his mind and threw her out.

If he was surprised that she didn't do an instant striptease he didn't show it.

She wasn't sure that he was even listening, but when she faltered under his apparent lack of interest his eyes flickered to hers and she pressed on. When she had finished, silence flooded back into the room.

'You're too expensive,' he said, at last.

'We're the best,' she countered, with relief. She found hard business a great deal easier to deal with than sexual innuendo.

'That's simply your opinion. And your business methods to date are not exactly reassuring.'

She refused to be drawn back down that path. Whatever he thought, she knew she had done nothing to apologise for, nothing to be ashamed of.

'I can give you references. The companies that we work for regularly . . . the ones who are astute enough to understand that you get exactly what you pay for . . . ' She couldn't resist the gibe.

'You're hardly likely to give me the name of anyone who was dissatisfied. I prefer to make my own judgements.'

She sat forward. 'I'm happy with that. Try us.'

He regarded her thoughtfully for a moment. 'I'll try you, Tara.'

She smiled then, glad of the opportunity to offer a rebuff to this infuriating man. 'I'm afraid I'm not for hire, Adam.'

'A pity.' He stood up and walked around the desk. 'Perhaps when you're ... ' he raised one mocking brow ' ... *astute* enough to grasp the opportunity I have offered you we can talk again.' He helped her to her feet and moved to the door.

Startled by the speed at which he had moved, Tara offered no resistance and was halfway to the door before she realised what was happening. She had been dismissed.

'But ... I can't. I have a business to run,' she protested. 'I never temp myself ... not since ... ' Her voice trailed away as his eyes challenged her.

'Perhaps you're afraid of putting

yourself on the line?' he offered, softly. He opened the door. Another moment and it would be too late.

'Certainly not!' Her mind was racing through the possibility he had presented and maybe it wasn't such a bad idea. No one was better able to demonstrate the quality of her agency; she measured all her girls against her own standards. Beth would have to manage the office for a week or so and she could catch up with her own paperwork in the evenings. He was waiting. Tara gave him a straight look. 'Very well, Adam. Thank you for the opportunity. May I assume that if I can meet the required standard you will give my company the first opportunity to fill your temporary vacancies on the terms I have outlined?'

'You may.' His smile was a challenge. 'But I warn you, my standards are very high.'

She lifted her chin and met him head on. 'So are mine. When shall I start and who do you want me to work for?'

'You start now, Tara. And you work for me.'

Tara realised that she should have seen it coming. Adam was watching her, his expression giving nothing away, waiting for her to protest. But she wasn't going to give him that satisfaction. She had sold her girls as the ultimate secretaries. Now was the moment to demonstrate all the calm, unflappable qualities of that breed.

'Certainly. May I ring my partner to explain?'

A spark of annoyance that kindled for a moment in his eyes was quickly masked, but Tara had seen it and felt a ridiculous surge of triumph. 'Of course. I'll show you to your office.'

He led the way to a hi-tech office next door to his own. 'You'll find everything you need in here. I'll give you five minutes to make your call and find your way around then you can bring in a notebook.' His eyes left her face and drifted down, absorbing every detail of her appearance from the snowy white stock at the neck, to the prim knee length skirt. He paused in the doorway, a faint smile curving his lips. 'You've taken so much trouble to look the part — is it too much to hope that you can actually take shorthand?'

'Shorthand?' Tara said, as if she'd never heard the word before. Her fingers gently touched the little gold brooch that fastened the stock at her neck. 'I expect I'll manage.'

'I'm afraid you'll have to do better than that,' he said, with satisfaction. 'Or you'll fail at the first hurdle.'

Tara tried the three telephones that lined the desk until she found one with a direct outside line and called Beth to briefly explain what had happened and arrange an evening meeting to organise working arrangements.

A quick exploration of a cupboard revealed a pile of stationery and she took a notepad and several pencils from a new box. She tapped on Adam's door and opened it.

'Ready?' He didn't wait for her

answer. She had hardly seated herself before he began. 'I want this retyped.' She recognised the report from the previous evening. He looked up. 'Preferably without any mistakes.'

'I'll do my best, Adam.' Her humble tone earned her a sharp look.

He worked swiftly through a pile of correspondence. 'Tell these people no. No. No. Ask for more details.' It went on. Eventually they reached the bottom of the pile and he leaned back and linked his hands behind his head. 'Now. I have a report that I need as soon as you can manage.' He raised an eyebrow in polite query. 'Today, perhaps?'

'Perhaps,' she agreed, half-hopefully, and once more received the benefit of a searching glance.

He began to dictate, without reference to notes and at such a speed that Tara wondered, in a brief moment when he paused for breath, if he was simply reciting from memory in an effort to have her begging for mercy. Her pencil flew over page after page until, at last, he reached his conclusion.

She looked up then, waiting for the next onslaught. 'Let me have a draft of that before you do anything else.'

'Is that everything?'

'For now. It should keep you busy for the rest of the morning.' He was dismissive.

'It's already half-past twelve,' Tara said, gently. 'And according to your secretary's diary you have an appointment at one o'clock with Jane.'

'So I have.' She made a move to go. 'Oh, and Tara, while I remember.' She paused before his desk. 'I don't want to see any of your admirers, desperate or otherwise, falling over themselves in my office. You will make certain they are all aware of that fact?'

Tara was in grave danger of losing her self-control. In danger of slapping Adam Blackmore's imperious, over-bearing face so hard that all chance of gaining his company's business would be lost forever. That thought alone kept the smile pinned to her mouth.

'I'll issue a bulletin for the one o'clock news. Just to be certain,' she said, her voice somehow retaining a teasing lightness she was far from feeling.

'There are so many?' A spark that might have been anger flashed in the shadowed depths of his eyes. 'I leave the method of broadcast entirely up to you, Tara. Just make sure you do it in your own time.'

'Yes, sir,' she said. But very quietly.

★   ★   ★

Tara did not consider the possibility of taking an hour for lunch. Or even half an hour. There was too much at stake. She spent the time instead familiarising herself with the word processing system before typing a draft of the report that Adam had dictated.

She found the original typist's version of the notes that needed corrections and ran that off too before hunger drove her in search of a sandwich. She had been gone barely fifteen minutes, but when she returned it was to find Adam Blackmore fuming in her office.

'Where the hell have you been?' he demanded, before she had hung up her coat.

'Lunch?' she offered.

He stared at his watch. 'Lunch! Is this the usual length of lunchbreak your so-called superior secretaries take?'

'About average,' she agreed. 'If you're looking for your report, I left the draft on your desk.'

He turned and walked into his office without a word.

'Thank you, Tara. You're a treasure, Tara,' she murmured to herself. Then she began to tackle the pile of correspondence he had given her. Despite an endless stream of interruptions from Adam she had finished by five. He threw the blotter of signed letters on her desk.

'When you've got those away you can go,' he said.

'Go?' For one appalling moment she

thought he had decided that one day was enough, but before she could protest that he hadn't given her a fair chance, he took the wind out of her sails.

'Yes. I want you ready for six-thirty. I've a meeting with the manufacturers for whom I prepared that report and I need you to take notes.'

'Oh, I see.' So far so good. 'Are you holding the meeting in the boardroom, or up here?'

'Neither. The meeting is in Hammersmith. I'll pick you up at home.' He paused in the doorway that connected their offices. 'It's not inconvenient, is it, Tara?'

'And if it is?' she asked.

His mouth curved in an insolent smile. 'Tough.'

He didn't wait to see the effect this response had on Tara, which was probably as well. She telephoned Beth to cancel their meeting then swiftly stuffed the envelopes with the mail, stamped it and put on her coat. She opened her office door and moved across to the lift.

'Still here?' She swung round to find Adam Blackmore, wrapped only in a short towelling robe, his dark hair damp and dishevelled from the shower, standing behind her. A matching pair of doors opposite his office stood half open to reveal a glimpse of the accommodation beyond. The significance of 'private apartments' suddenly struck her.

'You live here?' she asked. But she already knew the answer. It was little wonder he had thought she was pursuing him.

'Very good, Tara,' he said, his mouth twisted in a parody of a smile. 'Did you ever consider a career on the stage?' He didn't give her an opportunity to protest. 'I'll show you round when there's more time. We might even try that 'coffee' you were so keen on. Now we know exactly where we stand.' He leaned against the wall. 'I told you to leave half an hour ago. Why are you still here?' There was no denying the steely insistence underlying the velvet softness of his voice.

She swallowed hard. 'I had to change my own arrangements for this evening.'

His jaw tightened imperceptibly. 'I'm sure he'll wait. You are worth waiting for, aren't you, Tara?'

'You'll never know.'

There was a disquieting confidence about his smile. 'Use the private lift. It will take you to the side entrance on the ground floor.' He opened the door and offered her the key. 'I prefer to keep it locked. Otherwise all sorts of odd people can wander up.' He took her hand in his, pressed the key into her palm and wrapped her fingers around it. 'Now, I think you'd better go. Or you'll keep me waiting and that would be a big black mark against you, Tara Lambert. And I know you wouldn't want that.' He propelled her towards the small private lift and patted her bottom. 'Six-thirty. Not a minute later.'

Tara was still fuming as she stood

under a hot shower. Who on earth did he think he was? How could anyone work for such a man? Yet the neat stack of dated shorthand notebooks she had found in the cupboards suggested that the secretary she was standing in for had been with him for a long time.

The water was relaxing, taking the tension out of her neck muscles. He was testing her, that was all. Making sure she was what she claimed to be. And if he thought that she was prepared to use her body in the furtherance of business, she would disabuse him very quickly if he ever tried to put it to the test.

A little smile of satisfaction lifted the corners of her mouth. She had survived the first day. She had taken the worst he had been able to throw at her and come through more or less unscathed. Feeling decidedly more confident she grabbed a towel and began to dry herself vigorously.

She decided to wear a simple black jersey dress with long sleeves and a scooped neckline, elegant enough for the evening, but sufficiently understated for a secretary at a business meeting. She fastened the little gold brooch near her shoulder, tracing the simple shape with the tip of her finger; the outline of her name in shorthand. It was a reminder, a talisman against the aggressive charm of Adam Blackmore.

A peremptory ring at the bell summoned her to the door and she glanced at her watch. Precisely six-thirty. She hadn't doubted it for a moment. She picked up her coat and bag and opened the door.

He ran an assessing glance over her appearance and raised a sardonic brow. 'How very appropriate. Come along.' Tara made no comment. She dressed for the job she did. She knew that in many offices the staff were much more casual these days, even wore jeans, but she had her own very good reasons for preferring to keep her dress formal.

He led the way down the steps and ushered her into a sleek black Jaguar

XJS. Tara allowed her herself a smile as she fastened her seatbelt. The car so exactly suited her idea of the sort of car a twentieth-century knight might drive. A black knight. The analogy was so apt that she was forced to smother a giggle.

'What's so amusing?' he demanded.

She shook her head. 'Nothing.'

He stared for a moment as if she was quite mad, then shrugged and started the car. The conversation into London was a one-way affair in which he briefed her on the meeting, who was to be there and what notes he wanted her to take.

The journey home was accomplished in silence, with Adam deep in thought and apparently forgetting that he had Tara with him, he drove straight into the car park beneath Victoria House.

He caught her glance. 'I need those notes tonight, Tara. How long will it take?' He didn't bother to ask if she could do it. He simply expected that she would.

'Does your permanent secretary work

these hours?' she asked.

'Finding it too much for you already, Tara? Not got what it takes after all?'

She ignored this. 'What's the matter with her?' He frowned, not understanding the question. 'Your secretary. Jenny told me that she's on sick leave.'

'So you've met Jenny.'

'She came up to see me. She had the oddest idea of making me feel welcome. Explaining where everything was and telling me the names of a few people I might need to know.' She had also taken the trouble to explain that Adam rarely interfered with the running of his many business interests, leaving it to the bright young men he put in charge, offering advice only when it was applied for. He spent his time working on new ventures, developing new ideas.

'Oh, yes.' He wasn't in the least bit put out by her implied criticism. 'Jane is . . . ' He hesitated and Tara caught a flash of white teeth in the subdued light of the car park as if something had amused him. 'You mustn't worry. Jane is not suffering from anything infectious,' he assured her as he ushered her into the lift.

So his lunch appointment had been with his secretary. Clearly she wasn't that sick. 'That's not much comfort, Adam. Malnutrition isn't catching.'

'Sarcasm will get you nowhere with me, Tara. I am aware you haven't had time for a meal and I'll organise some supper for us upstairs. You can eat when you've finished.'

'Thank you.' But her dry tone drew no response.

The private lift whisked them swiftly to the penthouse suite and Tara went straight to her office and began to work. She was tired, hungry and ridiculously close to tears. It wasn't like her. But the day had been fraught with tensions, she had missed breakfast because she'd overslept and if she allowed herself to think about it too much she would begin to shake.

'How much longer?'

While she had been working Adam

had changed from his dark business suit. Now pale, well-washed denims stretched tightly across his hips and thighs, emphasising the arrogant maleness of the man. Tara dragged her eyes back to the printer. 'A couple of minutes.'

'Then leave it to print.' He took her elbow and guided her through the doors to his apartment and into another world.

His drawing room was vast. The pale polished floor seemed to stretch forever, interrupted only by Persian rugs and furniture that would have been equally at home in a modern art gallery. One wall consisted of the familiar arched windows beyond which the lights of the Thames Valley were spread beneath them. Opposite the wide white expanse was broken by an open fireplace where flames flickered over an enormous log. The fireplace was flanked on either side with a pair of Mark Rothko canvasses, huge subtle areas of colour that seemed to suck her in and wrap themselves around her mind.

Tara stopped in the doorway, silenced by the simple beauty of it.

'Well?'

'I . . . ' She couldn't think of any comment that did not sound banal and instead offered him the faintest smile. 'I was just wondering if you expected me to polish the floor in my spare time.'

His eyes gleamed wickedly. 'You won't have any spare time, Tara.'

'Oh?' Her smile was forced. 'You do realise that I charge by the hour?'

'And double after six o'clock, I have no doubt. I guarantee that I'll get every penny's worth,' he said. His buccaneer's eyes seemed to dance in the shifting light from the fire. Or perhaps she was just feeling light-headed for want of food. As if he could read her mind he led her across to a table laid for two and pulled back a chair.

'Help yourself, Tara,' he commanded and while she ladled rice and a rich, spicy beef dish on to two plates Adam poured the wine.

She ate slowly, with total concentration, savouring every mouthful, until, replete, she sat back with a little sigh.

'Do you feel better now?' he asked with apparent amusement.

Hunger pangs assuaged, she was prepared to be generous. 'Much,' she assured him.

'I'll pass your compliments to the chef.'

'You didn't cook it yourself?' she asked, in mock surprise. She propped her elbow on the table and rested her chin on her hand, her wide brown eyes regarding him with total innocence. 'Of course not. Silly me. Why would you bother to cook when you obviously own the wine-bar at the bottom of the lift shaft?'

'Why indeed?' Adam stood up. 'Come and sit over here.'

'I can't do that. There's the little matter of washing-up, or have you forgotten about getting every penny's worth?'

She gathered the dishes on to a tray and carried them through into a gleaming white galley kitchen. He followed her and took the tray from her hands. 'Leave them, Tara.' His smile was provoking. 'Eating time I'm prepared to pay for, but washing-up is strictly on your own time.' He slid his hand under her arm and led her firmly from the bright kitchen to the shifting, fickle light of the fire.

'It's real!' Tara exclaimed in delight and relieved to have an excuse to pull free of his disturbing fingers, bent down to hold her hands out to the flames. 'I thought it was one of those gas things.'

'I have no interest in fakes, Tara.' He waited until she curled up in a huge leather armchair, then handed her a brandy before stretching out in a chair opposite her, his long legs propped on the hearth. He sipped his drink. 'Of any sort.'

She cupped her hands around the glass and stared down for a moment at the pale liquid, watching the firelight strike sparks of amber from the crystal. Over dinner the evening had somehow ceased to be about business. This was not the office. This was the penthouse apartment of an attractive — her mind shied away from the blandness of the word. It was not an expression that evenly remotely applied to Adam Blackmore. She regarded him from beneath the screen of thick, dark lashes. There was nothing bland about him. He was as invigorating as standing beneath a mountain waterfall and had much the same effect on the ability to breathe. Her experience in such matters was limited, but she knew without any doubt that he was the most potently desirable man she had ever met and the most dangerous.

The evening had taken a subtle turn so that she had hardly noticed when they had moved away from business. And now they were sitting together before the fire sipping brandy in a manner that implied a perilous intimacy.

Tara put the glass down and straightened from the chair. Maybe this was an accepted part of his relationship with his permanent secretary. But there was a limit to how far she would go to take Jane's place. She was his temporary secretary. She wasn't prepared to take the same role as his lover.

'I'd better make sure that the printer hasn't jammed.'

He caught her hand as she moved quickly past him and spun her into his lap.

His eyes fixed her, held her momentarily in his power. 'The printer can look after itself,' he murmured, softly into her neck so the words vibrated against her skin and Tara knew that if she allowed her head to fall against his shoulder and parted her lips he would take everything she was prepared to offer and more.

But there had been something altogether too calculating in the momentary glimpse she had caught of his eyes before he closed them. She shivered. 'So can I,

Adam. But I'd prefer to get up without an unseemly struggle.'

He raised his head and she caught a gasp between her teeth. Whatever his original intentions, there was no doubting the desire that turned his eyes black in the shifting light of the flames.

It had been a long time since she had wanted to lay back in a man's arms. It was nearly seven years since Nigel's death and in all that time no one had broken through the shell she had erected to protect her heart.

Almost in panic she tried to move, but he held her firm and despite her brave words she knew that if he chose to keep her captive she would be hard pressed to free herself without resorting to the unforgivable. And she faced the disturbing truth that if he insisted upon kissing her she might never want to be free again.

For a moment his eyes challenged her to defy him, to ignore the warmth of his body against her own, to ignore the way his mouth curved with sensuous insolence, inviting her to make the first move and risk the surging desire that had surfaced so abruptly when he had kissed her in the wine-bar.

It was hard. Harder still to ignore the clamour of her blood pounding with wild impatience through her veins and the way her skin was tingling, begging to be stroked by the long fingers holding her against him, teased by the broad tip of his thumb, already far too close to a betraying nipple, erect against the soft cloth of her dress.

Another moment would have been a moment too long. But without warning he stood up with her, surprising a soft cry from her lips. He smiled then and set her gently on her feet.

'You're right, Tara. Better check the printer. Then I'll walk you home.'

Her hands were shaking as she shuffled the papers into some semblance of order. She managed to slip them into a folder and turned and held it as a kind of defence against him as he followed her into the office.

He took the file from her and threw it on to her desk. 'Come on. It's late.' He helped her into her coat, smiling as she pulled nervously away and quickly fastened the buttons. He summoned the lift and stood back to let her in. He paused with his finger on the button. 'I never gave you the promised grand tour.'

'I think I've seen more than enough,' she murmured, but she refused to meet his eyes.

'Enough for tonight,' he agreed.

They walked in silence along the quiet street and turned into the mews.

'I'll see you in the morning, Tara,' he said, and took the wayward strand of hair that never wanted to stay tidily in place and tucked it behind her ear. For a moment his fingers lingered there against the sensitive skin, threatening to upset the delicate poise of her equilibrium and pitch her into his arms.

'What time do you want me to start work tomorrow?' Tara asked, jerking away from his touch.

'Whatever time you arrive, my sweet, you can be sure I will already be at work,' he drawled, impudently aware of the effect he was having.

She risked a defiant smile. 'You don't really expect me to fall for that one, do you, Adam? I'll be there at nine. A fourteen-hour day is about my limit.'

'We'll see.' He bared his teeth in a smile and raised his hand in salute. 'Goodnight, Tara.'

She closed the door and leaned heavily against it for a moment, still feeling the dangerous heat of his fingers against her skin. Her hand strayed to the spot, then she pulled it away, furious with herself. Adam Blackmore was an arrogant, overbearing tyrant who knew nothing about her. He just thought she would make a temporary substitute in every way for his secretary, poor woman. Well, that wasn't her scene, she thought angrily. No matter how attractive, how desirable he might be.

She pushed herself away from the door. The first thing she needed was a warm drink if she was going to sleep. And every fibre of her being told her she would be needing all the sleep she could get. Every nerve-ending was jangling from a day in the presence of Adam Blackmore. She pulled a face. Every nerve-ending was jangling from a few moments curled in his lap, fighting all the instincts that urged her to wrap her arms around his neck and let him take her on that grand tour. Her fingers strayed to her little brooch. 'Some help you were.' She lifted the framed portrait from her mantelpiece and looked at it long and hard. The face that smiled back was unbelievably young, from another world when she was eighteen and life was very simple.

'Why did it have to be him?' she demanded. But the photograph had no answer and she replaced it with a sigh.

The light was winking on her answerphone, but she ignored it. It could wait until she had made her cocoa. She set some milk to boil and quickly changed into a pair of pink and white spotted pyjamas and slipped on a matching wrapper.

She put the cocoa on the coffee-table and walked across to the answerphone. She stared at it for a moment. It was probably nothing important. Nothing that wouldn't keep until the morning. Still. She pressed the button.

There was a sharp rap at the door. 'Drat the man,' she swore to herself. She flung open the door. 'Adam, this isn't funny . . . ' The words trailed away. 'Jim.'

'I have got to talk to you, Tara.' He pushed past her before she could close the door.

The answerphone recording clicked in and Beth's voice filled the room. 'Tara, Jim Matthews has been at the office again today. Blasted man actually offered me money to tell him where you live.' She chuckled. 'If he hadn't been so cheap I might have been tempted. I forgot to mention it when you phoned,

63

but I thought you'd better know that he hasn't given up.' The machine clicked off and began to rewind.

Tara turned on Jim Matthews. 'Have you any idea what time it is?'

'I've been waiting all evening to see you.'

'Waiting where?' she demanded. 'You weren't here when I got in.' Which, on reflection, she decided was probably just as well. Adam was not likely to be amused at having to send him packing two days running.

'Oh, I've been wandering around,' he said, absently. 'It's given me a great idea for a book. Have you any idea how terrifying those cat's eyes in the road are when they look up at you? Suppose they were real — have you got a notebook handy, I ought to make a few notes . . . '

'No!' Tara shuddered. 'And I don't want to hear about your horrible cat's eyes. It's time you gave up, Jim, and accepted the fact that I'm never coming back. You'll have to find someone else.

I'm not the only . . . ' She stopped as another thought struck her. 'How on earth *did* you manage to find out where I live? I'm quite certain that Beth wouldn't take your money, no matter how much you offered.'

'She was very rude, Tara. I was shocked to hear such language from a woman.' He sank on to her sofa.

'Well?' she demanded.

'There are always ways to find out things. You just have to think it through.' He shrugged. 'I wrote detective stories for a while, you know. I just imagined this was a detective story. How would my hero find out where the lovely lady lived?' He glanced at the table. 'Is that cocoa?' He picked up the cup and, ignoring her outraged protest, he began to drink it. 'This is wonderful. I'm absolutely freezing.'

'I'm not surprised. You're not wearing a coat.' She put her hands on her hips. 'You haven't answered my question.'

'It wasn't difficult. I just went to the

public library and searched through the electoral rolls.'

'Good lord!' His persistence stunned her. 'How long did that take?'

'Mmm? Oh, not long. I had narrowed the area down quite a bit. I knew which side of town, and that you walked, even when it was raining, so it couldn't be that far. But I admit that I was damned lucky you live in Albert Mews rather than Washington Lane.'

'Well, your luck just ran out, Jim Matthews. If you don't leave right now you had better prepare yourself — ' A thunderous knocking at the door stopped whatever she was going to say. 'What on earth . . . ?'

She ran to the door, fully expecting it to be her next-door neighbour with some emergency.

Instead Adam Blackmore burst through the door. 'Tara, are you all right?' He grabbed her arms, staring at her as if to reassure himself. 'I'd just got back to the penthouse and I realised I hadn't got the report you typed, so I went into the office.' He'd been running and he paused to catch a breath. He shook his head. 'I saw that man who was bothering you last night. He was headed this way. I know you said he wasn't dangerous, but he was walking down the middle of the road poking about in the cat's eyes. Quite odd, and I thought — '

He stopped as a movement behind Tara alerted him to the fact that she was not alone. He stepped forward as if to protect her, then halted as he took in the casual manner with which Jim had made himself totally at home on the sofa, feet propped upon the coffee-table, the mug of cocoa warming his hands.

His mouth a thin, angry line, Adam allowed his gaze to travel around the comfortable room, taking in every detail, the small circular window set into foot-thick walls, the posts and beams that framed the building decorated with bunches of dried flowers, the little red pot-belly stove in the hearth. It came finally to rest on Tara, her thick black hair tumbled about her shoulders, her feet bare, dressed for bed.

'I was concerned.' His eyes, dark and deep as a glacier, met Tara's. 'But I see that I needn't have worried.' His mouth managed a smile, but it didn't quite make it to his eyes. 'I told you he would wait.'

'Adam . . . '

He ignored her. He nodded, tight-lipped, at Jim. 'My apologies for the interruption.' Jim raised a languid hand in acknowledgement. 'I'll see you in the morning, Tara.' There was nothing reassuring in this utterance. Nothing reassuring about the careful way he shut the door on his way out.

Tara turned and stared at her intruder, wondering just what he had cost her. He looked so harmless, so insignificant, totally unaware of the havoc he had caused and the unaccountable misery that lay like a lump of lead in her stomach. 'Truly, Jim Matthews,' she declared with a sudden burst of anger, 'you are the most annoying man it has ever been my misfortune to meet.' But her words had no effect. Jim Matthews was blessed with that supreme selfishness that was so totally unconcerned with anything but his own desires that anger had no power to dent his complacency.

And the damage had been done. Getting angry with Jim could never change that. But when he repeated his suggestion that she marry him, she finally snapped.

'Don't you ever listen?' she demanded. 'No! No! No!' Something of her distress must have got through to him and he offered no further argument when she insisted that he must go. She would have demanded his promise that he never return. But she was too tired to bother and she was only too aware that it probably wouldn't make any difference if she did.

3

Exhaustion supplied the balm of sleep. But Tara had to drag herself into Adam Blackmore's private lift and it sped upwards far too fast in its eagerness to decant her on to the twenty-first floor the following morning.

And yet, as she took a deep breath and lifted her chin, she knew there was no point in putting it off a moment longer. She'd given it her best shot, but some things were just never meant to work. She tapped on his door and opened it. The room was empty. Having screwed herself up to face him, Tara felt suddenly angry.

She snapped the door shut and went into her own office. A pile of mail was waiting for her attention and attached to her VDU screen a little Post-it note simply said 'Carry on, Tara. I'll be in later.' She pulled it off the screen and stared at it for a moment. She checked the diary but it was blank and there was no clue as to when later might be.

'Carry on, Tara,' she said, to herself. She sat down rather suddenly on her chair. 'Just carry on. That's it?' She picked up a letter-opener and attacked an envelope. 'No, Tara Lambert. I doubt that. I doubt it very much.'

She began to open the mail and sort it for attention. Some she put to one side to deal with herself. Some would need his personal attention. One, a bill from a private London clinic for a Mrs Jane Townsend, would certainly need his personal attention, she thought a little grimly.

The phone rang at intervals, each time her ragged nerves springing to attention in case it was Adam. She took messages, answered queries where she could, and where she couldn't she found out who had the information. Gradually she began to assemble an idea of the impressive scope of Adam Blackmore's empire.

She was deeply engrossed in a copy of the annual financial report when a sudden warning prickle at the back of her neck made her look up.

How long he had been watching her was impossible to say. But the relaxed manner in which he was leaning against the frame of the door, his hands in his pockets, the silver streak of hair fallen across his forehead, suggested it had been some time.

'A little light lunchtime reading?' His voice, interrupting her thoughts, made her flinch.

'Is it lunchtime?' She glanced nervously at her watch. Anywhere but at his face. 'I hadn't realised it was so late. The morning has gone so quickly.'

'Really? I'm glad you weren't bored. Bring in your notebook; I'll do my best to keep you amused for the rest of the day.'

She gave him his messages and the mail. 'Is this all?' he asked.

'I dealt with the run-of-the-mill stuff. I've put copies of my letters at the bottom of the folder.'

'You take a great deal upon yourself,' he remarked as he flipped through her flimsies.

'You told me to carry on. If you simply want a shorthand typist, Adam, just say. I'll have a competent lady here within the hour.'

'I don't doubt it.' He raised his eyes briefly from the letter he was reading. 'But we'll leave things the way they are for the moment. A day is hardly sufficient time to judge whether you meet the required standard, is it?'

She compressed her lips into a straight line. What did the man want? Blood?

'Perhaps you could give me an idea of the timescale you have in mind? I do have a business of my own to run.'

He looked up then, giving her the benefit of his undiluted personality. It was not a comfortable experience. His scouring eyes seemed to ransack her mind, picking over the thoughts he found there and discarding them as completely without interest.

Then his eyes dropped back to the document in his hand. 'Until Jane gets back.'

Tara felt the heat rising in her cheeks and quickly looked down at her notebook. The next hour was spent in furious concentration until they were interrupted by a call on his direct line. He listened for a moment and then waved her away. 'That'll do for now.' She let out a long sigh of relief and set to work.

'Tara.' She visibly jumped as he appeared a few moments later in the doorway.

'Yes?'

'Book a couple of seats on a flight to Bahrain next week. Tuesday, I think.'

'Where do you want to stay?' She reached for a pencil.

'Our hosts will arrange accommodation. You only have to organise the flight.'

'Oh, right. Who's the other passenger?'

'You, my dear.'

The pencil snapped against the pad. 'Is something the matter?'

'No.' She swallowed. 'Of course not.'

His lips curled. 'No, I didn't think it would be a problem. You must want to work for me very badly, Tara. Just how far are you prepared to go, I wonder?'

'As far as Bahrain, apparently,' she said, sharply. 'I had assumed that Jane would be back by next week.'

'I'm touched by your concern,' he said, with heavy irony. 'But you needn't worry. There's nothing seriously wrong with Jane, other than a slightly raised blood-pressure. She's not ill, Tara. She's pregnant.'

'Pregnant!' His eyebrows rose at the sharpness of her response. 'I thought . . . ' She stopped. What she had thought was so dreadful that she couldn't even think the word. Relief brought a smile to her lips. 'Well, that is good news. But are you absolutely sure?'

'Yes, Tara, I'm absolutely sure,' he

said, with conviction. 'Why do you ask?'

'No reason, particularly. It's just that working for you — well, I can't imagine when she ever found the time.'

'Can't you?' His smile was wolfish. 'I'd offer to demonstrate right now, but I'm afraid I have a meeting that I can't avoid.'

Heat suffused her cheeks. 'I'm here as your temporary secretary. I don't have to prove whether I have reached the 'required standard' in any other subjects. Even if it comes under the heading 'double time'.' Even before the words were out of her mouth she knew she had made a stupid mistake.

He moved swiftly to her desk, his eyes snapping angrily as he caught her chin and forced it up.

'You're quite wrong there, Tara. In this job sex comes under the same heading as washing-up. You do it on your own time.' His mouth fastened upon hers with brutal determination. She struggled briefly, but first she was trapped by her chair, then trapped by the treacherous willingness of her lips to respond. But as they parted and she began to kiss him back, he abruptly straightened and stepped away from her, his green eyes glittering with anger. He strode swiftly to the doorway, but turned there, breathing heavily, as if he had just run up a long flight of stairs. 'Remind me to deduct that from your bill.'

* * *

For what seemed an endless time Tara sat fixed to her chair. Her hand hovered momentarily over the telephone. Then she withdrew it. Beth had enough to worry about without her partner going all weak and wobbly on her. The trip to Bahrain was purely business. He couldn't have made it plainer. And until the contract was in the bag she would simply have to keep her head and mind her tongue. No more late-night suppers in the penthouse. No more stupid remarks that gave Adam Blackmore openings to score the kind of point he had just made. The tips of her fingers brushed her lips, still tingling from the lightning raid he had made there. She withdrew them abruptly. It should be easy enough. She only had to think of Jane.

'Pregnant.' She repeated the word, recalling the conviction with which he had affirmed Jane's condition. He had been absolutely certain. Jenny Harmon must know, but hadn't said a word. She had merely said that Jane was taking some sick leave. There could be only one reason why it was a secret, why Adam was paying for her to attend a private clinic. A long sigh escaped her lips and she made an effort to move. It was none of her business after all. Jane wouldn't be the first secretary to have an affair with her boss, although not many husbands were accommodating enough to look the other way when a baby was involved. Unless her husband was no longer part of the equation and they were merely awaiting her divorce before she became Mrs Blackmore.

'It's none of my business.' This time she said the words out loud to remind herself more forcefully of this fact. She would simply have to forget that he had kissed her. That he had disturbed a thousand slumbering longings. The kiss had meant nothing at all to him. It meant nothing at all to her, she thought furiously. The fact that he had been able to draw such an eager response from her owed everything to his expertise. He probably spent all his spare time practising. With Jane.

She took a deep shuddering breath. Airline tickets first. She glanced down. Her hands were clenched together so hard that the knuckles had turned white. As she carefully straightened painful fingers she wondered just how long she had been sitting like that. Too long. She had a job to do and she'd better get on with it.

As she reached for the phone another thought occurred to her. He had said she would have to stay until Jane returned.

'Oh, dear God!' she moaned. It could be months. The situation was getting worse by the minute, and short of walking away from Victoria House and never coming back there seemed no way out.

* * *

'What's he like?' Beth Lawrence was curled up in the corner of the sofa, hugging a mug of coffee to warm her hands.

Tara sank into an armchair opposite and used the time gained to choose her words carefully. 'He's . . . difficult.'

Beth's eyes narrowed. 'Now that's interesting. I would have said that the man *you* can't tame with ruthless efficiency has yet to be born.'

'You're forgetting Jim Matthews. Perhaps I'm losing my touch.'

'Jim doesn't count.'

'No. Perhaps not. He's something of an original, after all.' She thought about this. 'But I think Adam Blackmore is an original too.'

'Original enough to be unmarried?'

'At the moment.'

'Oh?' Beth laughed. 'You've plans in that direction, then?'

'Don't be ridiculous,' she snapped, then buried her head in her cocoa to hide her expression.

'Just a joke,' Beth laughed. Then, more gently, 'I didn't mean to pry.'

Tara realised just how close she had come to betraying herself. 'There were no signs of a Mrs Blackmore in the penthouse anyway,' she added, carelessly, then blushed as Beth's eyebrows rocketed ceilingwards. 'I worked rather late last night and he gave me dinner.'

'How very kind,' Beth said, drily, but took pity on her partner and changed the subject. 'So how long will you be working for him?'

Relieved, Tara shrugged. 'I don't know. At least two weeks. We're going to Bahrain next week. Will you be able to manage the office on your own?'

'I'm going to have to manage, love. The bank manager asked me over for one of his little chats this afternoon. He's getting restless about the overdraft. Thankfully I was able to stall him with our dazzling prospects.' Beth caught sight of Tara's expression and frowned. 'It is going to be all right?'

Tara forced a smile. 'Of course it'll be all right.' It would have to be all right. 'I'm just tired. Jim turned up here last night and it took a while to dislodge him.' She didn't elaborate. She wasn't going to regale Beth with the heartwarming tale of Adam Blackmore rushing valiantly to her defence. His stinging little remark that evening still made her ears go pink.

He had made no reference to his precipitate arrival at her flat the night before. He had apparently decided that his need of her secretarial skills was more pressing than the small satisfaction he would gain in sending her packing. For a while she had even harboured the hope that he might choose to forget the incident altogether. In vain.

She had done everything he had asked without comment. Altered a financial report so many times that the figures began to merge before her eyes. Collected his cleaning. Made several hundred cups of coffee and in general been treated exactly like a rather slow-witted office junior. But by six-thirty everything had been done to his apparent satisfaction, although he hadn't bothered to say a simple thank-you.

'If there's nothing else, Adam, I'll go now.'

He kept her waiting for a full minute before he looked up from his writing block. She took this final insult without a murmur and finally he raised his head, fixing her for a moment with his eyes. Then he made a small gesture of dismissal. 'No, Tara. I really don't think that there's anything else I want from you. Run along home to your little love-nest.' The words, the gesture were meant to hurt.

It frightened her just how much he

succeeded in his intention. She had thought herself quite immune to the kind of casual sexual encounter he had intended. She had dealt easily enough with other men who saw the cool, efficient exterior as some sort of challenge to their manhood. But Adam Blackmore had caught her off guard and ruthlessly exploited the situation. And he had succeeded in keeping her off balance ever since.

'Tara?'

She started. 'Sorry, Beth, what were you saying?'

'Only that I thought I might have got through to him yesterday.'

'Him?' It took a moment for Tara to work out who Beth meant. 'Oh, Jim. Sadly, no. But I'd be interested to know exactly what you said to him. He professed to being shocked by your language.'

'Clearly not shocked enough.' Beth was defiant. 'But I did tell him that if he comes to the office again I'm going to call the police.'

'Oh, no. You mustn't do that!' Tara exclaimed. 'Promise me you won't do that. Can you imagine the publicity?'

Beth pulled a face. 'Perhaps it's not such a good idea.' Then she grinned. 'Now I'll be able to tell him you've left the country. That should head him off.'

'Only if you refuse to tell him where I've gone. I wouldn't put it past him to follow me.'

Beth laughed. 'I wish I could inspire such devotion.'

'No, you don't.' She wondered if Beth would think it quite so funny if she knew how close Jim had come to losing them any chance of working for Adam Blackmore. 'It's becoming something of a nuisance.'

Beth gave Tara a studied look. 'What is it?'

'Nothing. I . . . ' She couldn't possibly tell Beth her misgivings. 'I just wish I didn't have to go on this business trip. That's all.'

'Don't be silly. I'll manage here . . . Oh, I see. That's not it. Has the stunning Mr Blackmore made a pass at you?'

'How do you know he's stunning? I never said . . . '

'There was a piece in the *Financial Times* about him a few weeks ago. The photograph was a bit blurred, but it did its job. Don't dodge the question. Has he?'

'No. Well, yes.' She lifted her shoulders in a hopeless little shrug. 'To be honest, I'm not entirely certain.'

'I know you're a bit out of practice, love. But it's not usually that difficult to tell.'

'It was almost as if he was testing me. Except . . . ' She shook her head. So why had he come racing to her rescue? She forced a reassuring smile. 'He won't do it again.'

'Well, that's all right, then.'

Tara glanced at her partner, certain that she was having her leg pulled. 'Yes. It's strictly business.'

'Of course.'

'Will you stop doing that?'

'What's that, Tara?'

'You know very well. Surely you don't think I should have encouraged him?'

Beth pursed her lips. 'That's not for me to say.'

'So why do I have the feeling that you're going to anyway.'

'I have no idea. At twenty-five you're quite old enough to make up your own mind about whether or not to fall in love.'

'Don't be ridiculous.'

'There's absolutely nothing ridiculous about falling in love. It hurts. You want it to stop almost more than anything else in the world. Except not stopping. Listen to the voice of experience.'

'I know all about falling in love, Beth. What Adam Blackmore wants hasn't anything to do with falling in love.' Not the till death us do part sort of love. And that was the only sort she had ever been interested in.

Beth's glance strayed to the photograph on the mantel. 'You mean he's not a half-grown boy. He's a man and he's not going to be content with holding hands and gazing into your eyes. Beautiful though they undoubtedly are.' Beth shrugged. 'So, take all sensible precautions and enjoy yourself. When he breaks your heart you'll at least know you're still alive.' Tara's face drained of colour and Beth leapt to her feet and took her friend's hands. 'I'm sorry. My mouth was talking before my brain was engaged. Again.' Tara shook her head unable to speak.

'I'd better go.' Beth paused as if she would say something else, but changed her mind. 'Don't worry about the office. Everything's under control.'

* * *

Tara was pretty well under control too. She was far too busy to worry about Adam's motives during the next few days. He had at least stopped treating her like a useless junior and the workload before their trip had been so heavy that neither of them had had time to indulge in bouts of verbal fencing. Not that she was complaining about the extra hours. On the contrary, she welcomed the opportunity to demonstrate what she could do.

It was late on Monday evening when she took the completed sets of proposals into Adam's office. He swung around from his computer terminal as he heard her and his forehead creased in a frown. He glanced at his watch.

'What are you doing here? I thought you'd left hours ago.'

'You said you wanted these tonight. I've just finished binding them.'

He glanced at the pile. 'Very pretty. But tomorrow would have done just as well,' he added, carelessly, and apparently enjoyed the slight tightening of her lips which was the only outward sign of her fury. They both knew that their flight left before ten the following morning.

'Have you had anything to eat?'

'Eat?' She repeated the word as if it was some strange foreign expression that she was unfamiliar with.

'Apparently not,' he said, a little drily. 'Good. You can have dinner with me.'

She backed off nervously, furious with herself for betraying by one syllable the effect his undiluted attention had on her. 'It's all right. Really. I have to get home and pack.'

He didn't seem to hear her. Or if he did he ignored the words. He switched off the computer and came round the desk. If he saw her take a further step back he made no sign. 'I'm glad you're still here, in fact. I wanted to check over the last-minute details of our trip, so you can call it a working dinner. I'm sure your boyfriend will understand. He can cook for himself tonight.'

'If you're referring to Jim, I can assure you that he cooks for himself every night.'

Adam having edged her up to the wall took her coat from the stand and wrapped it around her and then, his arm still draped casually across her shoulder, he led her across the hall and summoned the lift. 'He doesn't live in, then?' he asked.

'No, he doesn't!'

'In that case I'll make sure our security people keep an eye on your flat while we're away.'

'There's no need.'

'I'll be the judge of that.'

Tara was too tired to argue. She had been working at full stretch for three days and all she wanted was to fall into bed. 'Thank you.'

The lift deposited them on the first floor and they took the escalator to street level and entered the wine-bar. The willowy blonde took their order and then left them alone.

'Have you ever been to the Middle East before, Tara?' She shook her head. 'It's interesting. The people are very friendly. Especially the men. It should suit you. You may even manage to — er — pick up some clients.'

Tara looked across at him. 'How did you break your nose, Adam?' she asked, finally.

He rubbed it thoughtfully. 'It wasn't an irate husband if that's what you're thinking.'

'No? I was rather hoping it might have been an irate secretary.' She stood up. 'There's still time. I'm afraid you'll have to eat both steaks yourself tonight, Adam. I've quite lost my appetite.'

She walked quickly from the restaurant and once outside broke into a run, desperate to get home, barely conscious of the tears pricking at her lids. 'Damn him, damn him, damn him.' She leaned against her door. Why on earth did he have to treat her like some sort of loose woman? She'd done nothing to deserve it. Only respond to the unexpected warmth of a stranger's kiss.

She sniffed and hunted in her pockets for her key. It wasn't there. Tara groaned. Of course it wasn't there, it was in her handbag. And her handbag was standing on her desk, exactly where she'd left it when Adam had bundled her into the lift. She ran back down the steps and knocked on her neighbour's door. There was no light and nobody came. She had already gone out for the evening and wouldn't be back until late. She never was. So much for leaving her spare key there for emergencies.

'This is an emergency!' she shouted at the locked door, needing to vent her frustration on something. It was unmoved by her outburst.

With the utmost reluctance she retraced her steps along the street and lowered herself once more into the seat opposite Adam.

His confident smile mocked her. 'Changed your mind?'

'No, I haven't. I've left my bag in the office. I haven't got a key.' He laughed. 'It's not funny,' she said indignantly.

'Yes it is. That the perfect — the *infallible* Miss Lambert should be human enough to forget anything is almost a relief.'

'If you hadn't rushed me out of the office . . . ' she protested, but he didn't let her finish.

'Never mind, the walk will have given

you an appetite.'

'I just want my bag, Adam.'

'Then you'll have to sit and watch me eat. Seems a shame.' The food arrived. He hadn't even bothered to cancel hers, so sure had he been of her return.

'Are you going to keep me here against my will?' she demanded.

He picked up his fork. 'Certainly not. You are quite at liberty to do whatever you wish.' His smile was infuriating. 'I'll bring your bag along later. When I've finished.'

She made one last appeal. 'You don't have to leave your meal. Just let me have your lift key.'

'Well, now. There's a switch. Usually you can't get enough of my company.'

'You are insufferable, Adam Blackmore,' she hissed.

'I know.' There was a cynical twist to his mouth. 'And I can't tell you what joy it gives me to see you suffering so thoroughly. You were doing it so well, so nobly, that I was almost ready to forgive you. Such a pity to spoil it with that little outburst of temper. Now you're going to have to start all over again.'

'I have done absolutely nothing that you need forgive me for!'

'No? Well, in that case you'd better put it down to simple envy. I had to work hard to get a start in business, Tara. I didn't have a pair of big brown eyes and a mouth that could turn even an accountant's head to win my way into the boardroom.' Apparently satisfied that he had reduced her to wordless rage, he continued. 'I'll give you your chance. I'd have given you that if you'd just knocked on my door and talked to me. Everyone deserves that. But you tried to take a short-cut and now you're going to have to work twice as hard to prove yourself.'

Tara blinked. She thought she was already doing just that. She knew it was too late to explain about Jim. Too late to explain about anything. It would only make things worse. She closed her eyes. How on earth could they get worse? But she had got herself into this

95

mess and if the only way out was by sheer hard work, well, she had never balked at hard work.

She picked up her knife and fork. 'You've got yourself a deal, Adam Blackmore.'

With the air cleared Tara found she could relax and enjoy her food. She sliced into the steak, suddenly very hungry indeed. Whatever Adam Blackmore did with Jane was no affair of hers; so long as he accepted that their relationship was on a purely professional basis she would be able to cope. Any lingering regret was futile. And throughout the meal she kept firmly on the subject of their forthcoming trip.

'Why Bahrain?' she asked, finally, allowing him to refill her wine glass. 'It seems rather a long way to go to raise the finance for a manufacturing plant in North Wales.'

'On the contrary. Offshore banking moved there in a big way when Beirut went to pieces. And there's a lot of oil money looking for a good home.'

'I thought it was all tucked up warm and cosy in snug little Swiss bank accounts.' She giggled. 'Or probably not so little.'

'And what would you know about Swiss bank accounts?' he asked, amused.

'Oh, nothing. I have enough trouble keeping my high street branch manager happy.'

This careless remark earned her a small frown. 'You shouldn't tell me things like that. It's not good business. If I suspected you were desperate for work I might decide to pressure you on fees.'

'You could try,' she offered, impetuously. Two glasses of claret had considerably helped with the relaxation.

He sat back in his chair and Tara was subjected to a long measuring look. She didn't flinch, although it took a very great deal of willpower not to look away from the amusement in eyes that challenged her to a game of financial chicken.

'You haven't been in business long,

have you, Tara?' He knew exactly how long she and Beth had been in partnership: not quite twelve months. She had told him herself. 'This recession must have been a blow and high street banks are notoriously short in the wind when the going is tough.' He spoke no less than the truth, but she managed to hold a smile and her tongue. She had already said too much. 'I wonder how tough it is?' He smiled briefly and her heart skipped a beat quite unnecessarily. 'I could find out, of course. Cut your rates to the bone. But I'll be generous.' He sat forward and suddenly his face was far too close and instead of work she was concentrating on the deep lines etched down his cheeks and the way his mouth curved at the corners. 'You can have all my business now, Tara, and go back to your safe little world down at street level . . . '

'Yes?' She waited for the *coup de grâce*.

'If you cut your rates by ten per cent.'

It was as if a bucket of cold water had been dumped on her head. He had no need to be envious of her big brown eyes. He had charm enough of his own to distract and bemuse the unwary. But this was a game and she must smile too, laugh off an offer that might well have tempted her a week ago. Before she had worked for him. He would pay for what he had put her through. Every last penny.

She propped her chin on her hand, refusing to back away from his raking eyes. 'Generous indeed, Adam,' she replied, her voice loaded with irony. 'And what are you prepared to forfeit in order to cover the reduction? Ten per cent efficiency, or ten per cent of the working day?'

He sat back and laughed. 'It's the status quo, then? You are so confident?'

'I have reason to be. And you have nothing to lose, Adam.' But she had. Her peace of mind, a certain tranquillity that while it didn't seem quite so attractive as it once had, had to be safer than this roller-coaster ride her body took whenever he chose to exert his charm. 'But I think we're going to have to put a time limit on this trial period. It certainly wouldn't be good business to allow you to keep me working for you indefinitely as a hostage to fortune.' She smiled sweetly. 'Would it?'

He returned her smile with interest. 'Shall we fetch your handbag? You did say you were anxious to get home to pack.'

'So I did.' His change of subject didn't worry her. She hadn't expected an immediate answer, but she had made her point. He pulled back her chair and opened the restaurant door for her.

'You'll need an evening dress, by the way. I should have said earlier, but I imagine you've got some neat classic to cover every eventuality in your wardrobe?'

This totally accurate summation of the clothes she wore to work irritated Tara. Of course she kept her clothes simple. No one wanted a secretary who flashed and jangled, but he made it sound like a failing. As if she had no imagination.

She retrieved her bag from her office and located her key. 'I'll see you in the morning, Adam. Thank you for dinner.'

'It's late. I'll walk you home.'

'Do you walk Jane home?' she asked, before she considered the wisdom of such a question.

His brows closed in a slight frown. 'There's no need — ' The phone began to ring. 'Hold on.' He lifted the receiver. 'Adam Blackmore.' A warm smile creased his face. 'Jane!' There was genuine pleasure in his voice. 'Did you? I went down to the wine-bar with your replacement for a bite to eat.' His eyes flickered across to Tara. 'No competition, princess. She wears her skirts too long.' He laughed at something Jane said, then, more serious, he asked, 'What did the quack say?' He sat himself on the edge of her desk and Tara turned and walked quickly to the lift. The door slid open immediately and although she heard him call her name she didn't look back, but stepped inside and pressed the button.

For the second time that evening she ran the length of Victoria Road and didn't stop until her own front door was fastened behind her.

She knew what kind of man Adam Blackmore was. A ruthless, single-minded man who would use her and throw her away whenever it suited him. She was every kind of a fool to even think about him. But the sharp stab of pain that had jabbed like a knife into her chest when he had said, oh, so casually, that Jane didn't need to be walked home. Tara banged her fist against the wall and fought back the stupid, humiliating tears. How could she have been such an idiot to even mention it. Jane was the perfect secretary. One who never went home.

Her phone rang. She knew it was him. No one else would ring her this late. For a moment she considered leaving it to the answering machine. Then she grabbed the receiver. If he thought she hadn't got home safely he might just come to check and she was in no mood to face him.

'Tara Lambert.' There was no answer. 'Hello?'

'That sounds marginally more friendly.' His voice was grim. 'I just wanted to be sure that you got home safely. Why didn't you wait for me to take you?'

'There was no need. I walk home from work every evening by myself.'

'At eleven o'clock?'

'Well, no,' she allowed. 'But then I'm not quite the slave-driver you are.' There was silence at the other end of the line. 'And I am quite capable of looking after myself.'

'Is that right?' His low voice vibrated into her bones. 'I'll bear that in mind. But you'd better hope there's someone else around next time you're in need of a knight errant.'

She gasped. 'Some knight errant!'

'Better than you know, Miss Tara

Lambert. Better than you deserve.'

'How dare you presume to judge what I deserve? You know nothing about me. Nothing! And I wish you'd stop calling me Miss Tara Lambert in that patronising tone of voice.'

'I'm not — '

'If you're going to patronise me, at least get it right.' Her voice broke on a sob. 'It's Mrs. Mrs Tara Lambert.' She let the phone drop back on to the cradle and let out a long shuddering sigh. Stupid. Why had she done that? Simply to score a point? A cheap, meaningless point. The phone rang again but she ignored it and when the machine cut in the caller hung up. She wondered briefly if he would come hammering at her door. It didn't seem likely.

Tara looked across at the photograph on the mantel. 'I'm sorry, Nigel,' she whispered. But what she was sorry for, exactly, she couldn't have said.

She had a bath, staying in the water until the chill drove her out. Then she surveyed the open suitcase on her bed. She would have to go with him if he still wanted her. It was too late to brief anyone else. She was a professional, took a pride in her work and that was all that was left to her. Pride.

She folded her neat, sensible clothes, so exactly right for the office. And her underwear. Not so sensible. She picked up her swimsuit and shrugged. She didn't know if she would have the chance to swim, but it took up no room. Then she looked at her evening clothes. She had two really good dresses. One plain black. Elegant, classic, boring. The other was brilliant scarlet silk, exactly like an Oriental poppy. She packed the scarlet silk.

4

The 'Boarding' sign for the flight to Bahrain appeared on the monitor, and Tara let out a silent breath of relief and moved towards the gate indicated.

Adam had barely spoken to her since he'd picked her up in the chauffeur-driven limousine at just after eight that morning. She had been waiting in a neat black suit, plain low-heeled shoes, the minimum of make-up and her hair in its customary chignon. The perfect secretary, discreet to the point of invisibility. To the casual glance she could have been almost any age.

But it took the interested observer no time at all to absorb the fair, flawless skin, the frank brown eyes, a generous mouth that the merest skim of lip gloss had done nothing to accentuate. Only the faint shadows beneath her eyes suggested that sleep had not come easily.

He picked her up at eight, the harsh ring on the bell doing brutal things to her nerves so that her hand shook as she reached for the door-handle. But she had painted a non-committal smile upon her face and opened it.

He was dressed comfortably for travelling, as she would have been if she hadn't needed the armour of her working clothes. Casual trousers and a light sweater over his open-necked shirt were a stark contrast to her black and white formality. For a moment they both stood perfectly still while his eyes ransacked her face, demanding some response from her. Tara's cool, polite mask almost cracked beneath his seeking eyes.

The silence went on so long that his voice, when he spoke, was like an electric shock.

'You are coming then? Mr Lambert, I take it, has no objections?' He looked over her head into the interior of her apartment as if challenging him to appear.

A touch of colour lit the fine bones of her cheeks. 'Mr Lambert is in no position to object,' she said, quietly.

'Then we'd better go.' He picked up her suitcase and without another word walked down to the car.

She followed him and climbed into the back, hoping that he might decide to sit beside the driver. No such luck. He slid alongside her, filling the ample space with his broad figure, leaned back and closed his eyes.

Someone had to make an effort to restore the possibility of a civilised working relationship or the journey would be a nightmare. 'The flight is on time. I checked.'

'As always, you are totally efficient, Mrs Lambert.'

'Please don't — '

'Why not?' She flinched as he stabbed the words at her, fixing her with wintry eyes. 'I'm only responding to your request, after all.'

She didn't answer and, apparently satisfied, he closed his eyes again. They completed their journey in silence and checked in at Heathrow, accomplishing the formalities without delay.

Adam hesitated as he handed back her passport, glancing at the name, Mrs Tara Lambert, printed neatly in the space provided and then flickering a glance at her pale face. Her outburst the previous evening had at least saved her the embarrassment that would have resulted from his more public discovery. Except that she could simply have told him that she was a widow and instead of that cold dislike his eyes might have softened with sympathy. She closed her eyes momentarily. Much better this way. His sympathy was the last thing in the world she wanted, she thought unhappily. His dislike was infinitely safer.

Their bags disappeared along the conveyor and the clerk handed Adam their boarding cards.

'Would you like some coffee?'

Startled by the unexpected normality of his offer, she shook her head. 'No, thank you.' She made a move towards the book stall. 'I'll just get something to read.' She couldn't imagine being able to concentrate for more than a minute on anything, but a book would make the likely silence during the long flight less noticeable.

He watched as she nervously turned a carousel filled with paperbacks. She came to an abrupt stop at the sight of a particularly garish cover. Adam raised an eyebrow and lifted the book from the rack.

'I wouldn't have thought this was your cup of tea, Mrs Lambert.' He regarded her steadily for a moment. 'Much more the Jane Austen type, I would have thought. Do you want this?'

'I've read it, thank you.' Cover to cover, at least twenty times.

'Have you now?' He held on to it. 'You're all surprises, Mrs Lambert. I'll have a look at it myself; it might provide me with some clues.'

'I said I'd read it. Not that I had enjoyed it.'

'Even more interesting.' He turned the book over and examined the back cover, frowning slightly. Then he gestured at the carousel. 'Is there anything you want there?'

She shook her head. 'No, thank you. I'll just take a magazine.' She scooped up a couple, hardly looking at the covers and found him waiting at the cash desk. She surrendered them unwillingly. But he appeared for the moment to have lost interest in baiting her and didn't even look to see what she had chosen. The flight call was a welcome interruption and they walked through Passport Control and along the wide corridor to their gate.

The stewardess settled them in their seats. It was the first time that Tara had flown on anything but a charter flight and the amount of space in the first-class cabin on a scheduled airliner came as something of surprise. After the flurry of take-off she looked around with interest.

'Is this the first time you've flown?'

Adam asked, watching her.

'No. But this is a long way from a package holiday to Greece.'

'Was that where Mr Lambert took you on your honeymoon?' he asked, so casually that for a moment she thought she hadn't heard correctly.

'I beg your pardon?'

'Greece. Is that where — ?'

'No.' She deliberately opened a magazine and stared blankly at the page in front of her, although she couldn't for the life of her have said what was on it.

He shrugged. 'Where was he this morning? Discreetly out of sight?' When she didn't answer he picked up her left hand, effortlessly resisting her efforts to pull away, and laid it flat across his own much larger one. 'Only I couldn't help noticing that you don't wear a ring.'

'It's . . . too big. It kept falling off.' She had been so much rounder as a girl. The weight had disappeared as suddenly as the shock of Nigel's death and it had never returned. She looked him full in the face. 'I was afraid of losing it.'

'You could have had it taken in. So helpful to know exactly where you stand.'

'For whom?' Tara suddenly realised that her hand was still lying in his and snatched it away. 'It doesn't bother you, surely, one way or the other? And I know I'm married.'

'You have a very odd way of showing it, Mrs Lambert. And I disapprove of lying.'

'I have never lied to you.'

'No? I did ask you if that poor besotted fool was your husband.'

'And I told you that he was not. And that's the truth.'

His mouth pulled down into a line that showed his distaste and he flicked a finger at the back of the book he had bought in the airport, where to her horror she saw Jim Matthews' photograph. 'So this is just the boyfriend. I wonder if there is a word for the male equivalent of a harem?' he wondered, almost idly.

'I've no idea.' Tara was angry. He had no right to judge her. 'But considering I wear my skirts too long,' she went on, 'I don't do so badly, do I?'

'You — ' He checked himself and almost smiled. 'Not badly at all. Perhaps I should be grateful for the body armour you wear. If you were really trying I have no doubt that you could cut swathes through the male population.' He captured the curl that never would stay confined by her ruthless pins and wound it around his finger. 'In clinging pink silk with this black cloud of hair loose about your face, who could possibly resist you?' He tugged his finger free and the sharp pain at her temple brought the prick of tears to her eyes. He thrust the book in front of her at the dedication page. The words leapt out at her. 'To Tara — my inspiration'. 'I wonder what you did to earn that, Mrs Lambert? Perhaps the text will help me to find out.'

Tara blanched. There would be all too many clues of the kind he was looking for. That was the reason she had refused to work for the wretched man ever again despite his pleas. 'The only inspiration he had from me was that I didn't slow him down when he was in full flow. I took down every horrible word in shorthand.'

For a moment his eyes held hers and for a moment she thought he believed her. Then he shrugged. 'I think I'll read it anyway.'

The stewardess offered them drinks but Tara followed Adam's example and took only a mineral water. And she refused lunch. Adam picked at his, then pushed it away and picked up the book again, apparently fascinated by the sheer awfulness of it. Tara gave up trying to read and stared down at the clouds.

The plane droned on, leaving behind the occasional green glimpses of Europe. They were now flying over the desert which offered only a rare glimpse of an isolated green patch to conjure up pictures of a romantic oasis with black tents and blacker stallions and fierce, handsome men. Far from the truth Tara suspected, but still, exciting.

She glanced at her watch. An hour to go. She wanted to freshen up before landing, but Adam's face was so forbidding that she hardly dared interrupt his concentration to ease past him. But as if he could read her mind he drew back his long legs.

'Thank you.'

He glanced up then, from his book. 'You only had to ask, Mrs Lambert.'

She took a little time tidying her hair and make-up to give herself a breathing space. Once they arrived on the island she knew work would take up all her time. Meetings every morning and a variety of social events had been arranged for the evenings. She would prepare the notes in the afternoon and that would be that. But somehow the next hour had to be got through.

She gathered her things and began to walk slowly back to her seat.

'Please hurry back to your seat and

fasten your seatbelt,' the stewardess warned her. 'There's some turbulence ahead.' At that moment the seatbelt signs came on and the captain spoke over the intercom briefly, to warn them. She waited for Adam to move his legs and let her by, but he just looked at her.

'Please may I get to my seat?' she asked, forced to play his game.

He smiled then. 'Of course.' But before he could move the plane lurched and threw her off balance. She would have fallen, but he reached for her and caught her as she fell, gathering her in and holding her in his lap.

'I'm sorry,' she said, trying and signally failing in her attempt to ignore the warmth of his chest beneath her hands, the closeness of his face to hers.

His eyes were brilliant in the clear bright light at thirty thousand feet. Clear and green and bottomless. 'Don't be sorry, Mrs Lambert. It was my fault you weren't safely in your seat.' She watched, fascinated as the corners of his mouth creased in a smile. 'And if you had fallen and hurt yourself you would have been no use to me.' She stiffened and he laughed. 'It's going to be a desperate trip if we keep this up, Mrs Lambert. What do you say to a ceasefire?' His brows rose in query. She wanted to free herself. And it wasn't as if he was holding her tight. But a languor seemed to have invaded her limbs, making it quite impossible. It wasn't fair, she thought, desperately, that one man, the wrong man, could have such a disastrous effect on her. 'Well? What do you say?'

'Pax?' she offered, softly, but refused to meet his gaze.

He turned her chin gently, so that unless she closed her eyes she had no choice but look at him and for a long moment he studied her face. Then he caught the nape of her neck and pulled her down, so that for the pause of a heartbeat his lips brushed against hers. 'Pax,' he murmured, and before she knew what had happened she was sitting safely in her own seat once more.

She was trembling. She looked at her hand grasping the armrest and wondered if he knew what he had done to her. But he had returned his attention to the book. Apparently it was all inside and she had managed not to betray herself totally.

The captain announced that they would shortly begin their descent to Bahrain, the weather conditions and the temperature.

The bustle of arrival covered any remaining awkwardness and by the time they had cleared Customs, Adam was able to introduce her to the dark, smiling man who met them without any apparent problem as Mrs Tara Lambert, laying the faintest emphasis on the Mrs.

'Tara, this is Hanna Rashid.' The man took her hand and raised it to his lips. 'We spoke yesterday on the telephone, did we not, Madame Lambert? Such a beautiful voice.' Despite his French accent and his European clothes, his complexion was dark, his moustache thick and silky. He was exotically foreign and his black eyes suggested that he was her slave. He ushered them through the Arrivals hall and out to the car. 'And how is the lovely Jane?' he asked Adam as she walked ahead. 'Such a pity she could not join you on this visit.' His voice had dropped, but not sufficiently for the discretion he had so evidently intended. She didn't catch Adam's reply, only Hanna Rashid's soft laughter.

Their luggage was stowed in the back of a large white Mercedes and Hanna whisked them away from the musty, unpleasant smell that assaulted them once outside the air-conditioned airport buildings, across the causeway and into the darkness of the open desert.

Tara looked around her, wondering where they were going, but the men were deep in conversation and she did not wish to interrupt. They passed buildings illuminated by thousands of lights that outlined the walls and then finally Hanna drove through gates into the courtyard of a large house.

'You should be comfortable here, *madame.*'

Tara smiled. 'I hadn't realised we were to be your guests, Mr Rashid. I assumed we would stay at an hotel.'

'But no. You will be more private at the villa.' He opened the door and helped her out. A servant immediately appeared and unloaded the baggage.

At the door Hanna offered his hand. 'We will meet later, for dinner, when you have rested.'

Tara frowned. 'But, I don't understand . . . ' Something in Adam's face made her stop.

'There's a car in the garage, Adam. We'll see you at about ten?'

'Thanks, Hanna.' He put his arm around Tara's waist and swept her inside. The door closed and she turned on him.

'What — ?'

'This is Hanna's summer home. Even in winter his British guests find Manama a little humid.'

'But I can't stay here alone with you.'

'No?' He stood back to let her enter a beautifully furnished drawing room. 'You'll be quite safe, Tara. I'm fussy about sharing.' He helped himself to a drink and offered her one. She shook her head, speechless. He drained his glass. 'Shall I show you to your room?'

'No, thank you. I'm sure I can find it myself.'

He shrugged. 'Well, don't get lost.'

His warning was unnecessary. The elderly man-servant who had taken their bags was waiting to conduct her to her room. But the villa was far larger than she had realised and left to her own devices she might never have found it. It had been built on two floors surrounding a courtyard garden in which a small fountain splashed seductively. All the upstairs rooms opened from a covered veranda overlooking this, which now the sun had set was illuminated with concealed lighting.

Tara unpacked her bag and took advantage of the luxurious en-suite bathroom, pampering herself with bath oil to soak away the dried-out feeling from the pressurised atmosphere of the aircraft. Then she sorted out something to wear. They were having dinner at a nightclub in Manama and, since she had no idea how dressy it might be, settled on a plain 'little black dress'. Adam would curl his lips, but she told herself she didn't care. With a practised twist she fastened her hair into its familiar chignon. Anything else would undoubtedly bring down an accusation of flirting from Adam. And she applied only a little more make-up than she would normally wear to the office.

She slipped off her cotton wrap and briefly examined her reflection. Tara had never been able to resist beautiful underwear. The fine satin and lace of her flimsy teddy drew a smile of genuine amusement to her lips, as did the black stockings. Then she covered it all with a plain black crepe evening dress, which had done duty at more dull functions for more companies than she could remember. The joys of being a temporary secretary.

She glanced at her watch. It was a little after nine. She had no wish to join Adam downstairs and be tormented by his barbed comments, but neither did she relish sitting in her room. She had noticed a stairway down into the garden and decided to explore a little.

The evening was cool, but not unpleasantly so after a British winter and there was a delicate scent in the air that drew her down the path in search of the flower that made it. When she reached the little fountain she sat beside it, listening to the pleasing sound of water.

'It's quite lovely, isn't it. A concealed garden to protect the women from the gaze of lustful men.' His voice out of the shadows made her jump. 'Hanna Rashid is a charming man. But despite his French manners he is an Arab. They have different ways. Their women are protected from casual encounters, but the men are quite happy to take advantage of the freer attitudes of European women. You would do well to remember that.'

Her eyes flew wide open. Surely he wasn't suggesting that this was a . . . ? Of course not. He was teasing her. 'I have no idea what you mean.'

'Oh, I think you do.' He sat beside her, starkly compelling in the severest dinner-jacket, the simplest of dress shirts. No ruffles, no wing collars to bolster this man's ego. 'But if you want me to spell it out for you, my lady, then I will. Just so there are no misunderstandings.' He lifted his hand to her cheek and touched it very gently. She kept very still, knowing instinctively that this was not a threatening gesture, that just for a moment she was quite safe. He turned her face towards his. 'While Hanna Rashid believes you are here for my pleasure, Tara, you will be safe from his attentions.'

His hand was suddenly burning a brand on her cheek. 'Is that what you told Jane?' some devil compelled her to ask.

His mouth straightened in a thin line. 'In her case it wasn't necessary.' He stood up abruptly. 'It's time we went.'

She fetched her bag and a stole and by the time she had found her way to the front entrance the car was waiting. He opened the door for her and then climbed in and on the way into the city reminded her of the people who would be at dinner with them: an American banker and his wife, a couple of local businessmen, Hanna Rashid. She barely listened. She had memorised all the names before they left. Instead she dwelt on what he had said in the garden. So long as he believed she was there for Adam's pleasure.

Maybe some businessmen took their secretaries away for 'pleasure'. He had made it crystal-clear that Jane had been happy enough in her position. But she wasn't a pleasure girl and she wasn't about to let anyone think she was.

Hanna met them at the restaurant

door and welcomed them. As he bent over Tara's hand, she caught Adam's cynical eye watching them and when the man straightened, she rewarded him with a brilliant smile, allowing him to take her arm and introduce her to the other guests.

Somehow she found herself seated at one end of a long table, with Adam on the opposite side at the other. But Hanna kept her entertained, asked her about her life and managed to extract a great deal more personal information over the period of several hours than she realised she had parted with. But when the floor-show ended and the dancing started Adam was at her side before Hanna could move.

'Tara?'

She very nearly refused, but one look at his face was enough to immediately disabuse her of any such notion. 'Thank you, Adam.'

He took her firmly in his arms and began to dance. 'What the hell did you two find to talk about all evening?' he demanded under his breath.

'Nothing of any importance. He's very amusing.'

'He's also very clever. I hope you weren't discussing business.'

She leaned back slightly. 'I'm not a complete idiot, Adam. I know when I'm being pumped for business information.'

'I hope so.' He pulled her close again. 'So what did you talk about?'

'Life, love, poetry,' she teased.

'A loaf of bread . . . a flask of wine . . . thou . . . ?'

'That sort of thing,' she agreed, nonchalantly

'Well, don't complain that I didn't warn you.' The music stopped and he returned her to Hanna, who immediately claimed the next dance. But it wasn't the same. The man danced superbly, he was amusing and charming, but he wasn't Adam. Adam was dancing with the American woman, making her laugh, being amusing and charming to her. She sighed and Hanna was immediately all concern.

'You are tired, *chérie*?' he said. 'It has been a long day for you. Let me take you home.'

A spark of alarm suddenly penetrated. 'Oh, no, thank you. I'd better wait for Adam.'

'Surely you are off duty now?' he said. 'And Adam is going to be a while, I think,' he said, a slight edge to his voice. Tara glanced around and both Adam and the American woman had apparently disappeared. She went very cold.

'I am tired. I shall be delighted to accept your offer, Hanna. Thank you.'

She bade goodnight to the rest of the party and allowed Hanna to usher her into the lift. He took her hand and she stiffened, but he made no other move on her and she gradually relaxed.

He settled her in the front seat of his beautiful Mercedes and then drove slowly through the desert night, pointing out the constellations that seemed so much closer than at home.

'Tomorrow afternoon I will take you out into the desert and show you what it is really like, beautiful Tara. But tonight, you need to sleep.' They were at the villa now and he helped her from the car as if she was the most fragile bloom. A final touch of his lips to her hands and then he was gone.

She unpinned her hair and shook it loose. So much for Adam's warning. She smiled as she unzipped her dress and stepped out of it. She slipped it on to a hanger and was putting it away when there was a sharp rap on the door and Adam's voice rang out.

'Tara!' In her underwear, she hesitated. 'Tara! Are you there?'

She grabbed a wrap and held it in front of her before opening the door. 'Yes? What is it?'

'So you're back. Are you alone?' he demanded, his face a mask of anger.

'Of course!' But Adam swung around the door, not convinced.

'What on earth made you leave . . . ?' The words died away as Adam

Blackmore took in the vision before him. Tara, her pale face surrounded by a cloud of dark glossy hair, her figure more revealed than covered by the delicate lace that clung softly to the firm contours of her breasts and swooped over the flare of wide, sensuous hips, stepped quickly back, but only drew attention to long legs encased in fine black stockings.

She clutched at the wrap in an attempt to cover herself. 'Get out!'

He made no move to go. Instead he plucked it from her trembling fingers and flung it to the other side of the room and drank his fill. He finally dragged his eyes back up to her face, white but for two hectic spots of colour staining her cheeks. 'You do well to keep it under armour plating, Mrs Lambert. Mr Lambert is a lucky man. You can tell him I said so.'

He turned and walked quickly from the room, closing the door behind him. She flew to it, turning the lock and standing with her back to it as if that

131

would keep him at bay if he tried to break the door down.

Then she shook her head. 'Stupid!' she said, quite softly to herself. If she had held out her hand to him he would have been unable to help himself. But she had no practice in the art of seduction, despite everything he thought of her. And probably that was just as well. There was Jane and her baby to consider, after all.

The following morning she dressed to dampen any thoughts of lust. She screwed her hair up tighter than ever and wore a severe navy linen dress. Adam followed her into the dining room and helped himself to coffee.

'This is an Arab breakfast. If you want eggs the cook will prepare them for you.'

'This is fine, thank you.' She helped herself to yoghurt and pitta bread and coffee, not quite feeling up to tomatoes and goat's cheese.

'Did you sleep well?' he enquired, politely.

'Yes,' she lied. 'Did you?'

He raised his head to look at her. She knew he wasn't seeing the navy dress, but what he imagined, with a good deal of justification, was beneath it. 'What do you think?' He apparently did not expect an answer, since he immediately launched into a discussion of the day's programme.

'We have a meeting at the bank this morning. It should be over by twelve and we'll have lunch, then work here this afternoon. There's a cocktail party at the British Embassy this evening and then a change of plan. We've been invited to dinner with the commercial secretary and his wife.'

She made a note in the diary. 'When did you arrange that?'

'I saw Mark at the restaurant last night when he was on the point of leaving and walked with him to his car.' His look made her flinch. 'I was gone all of five minutes, quite long enough apparently for Hanna to talk you into a look at the desert by night. But then a blind man could have seen you wouldn't take much convincing.'

'But he said . . . ' She stopped, unwilling to betray herself. If she admitted to leaving because of Hanna's implication that Adam was otherwise engaged he would know just how vulnerable she was.

'Yes?' he prompted.

'He was a perfect gentleman.'

'How disappointing for you. But then, he hasn't seen you in your underwear. Yet. I can guarantee he won't manage my self-restraint.'

'If Hanna Rashid sees me in my underwear, Adam, it will be at my invitation.'

'You're playing with fire, Tara.' He stood up, his breakfast half eaten. 'But you're a grown woman and hardly my responsibility.'

'And you need me too much to send me packing, no matter how much you'd like to.'

His look was a warning that she was on the edge of insolence, but Tara knew that they had long ago stepped across the boundary that should remain in any professional relationship. And she knew without doubt that but for Jane she would already have taken Beth's advice to enjoy herself. Adam Blackmore had already managed to go a fair way to breaking her heart, and all the pain and none of the pleasure seemed a little hard.

The day proceeded very much according to plan. Hanna Rashid was there, but in the background and Adam casually seated himself alongside Tara, cutting out the other man at lunch.

There was a well furnished office at the villa and Tara spent the afternoon typing up her notes and dealing with correspondence, while Adam was on the telephone.

At four Hanna Rashid arrived, to Adam's ill-concealed annoyance. 'But I promised the beautiful Madame Lambert I would show her the desert. The sunset.'

'Then it will have to be some other

time, Hanna. She's here to work and she's too busy to go gallivanting off to look at the sunset. Or any other interesting things you might have in mind to show her.'

He looked at Tara and shrugged. 'Another time,' he promised. And his eyes told her it would be soon. His smile would break your heart, she thought, if you were fool enough to believe it. She smiled back warmly, but only because she knew it would make Adam furious.

She paid for that smile with an onslaught of work that left her lying in the bath at six-thirty, trying to recoup sufficient energy for the long evening ahead.

She wore a dark red evening suit, the skirt a little shorter than usual. It wasn't part of her business wardrobe. There was a limit to that. And she was rewarded with a faint smile when she descended to the drawing room.

'Hanna won't be there this evening, Tara,' he reminded her.

'I know.'

'Then isn't that rather a waste?'

'If that's supposed to be a compliment, Adam, thank you.'

'Any time. A drink?'

'A gin and tonic, please.' He handed her a tall frosted glass. 'Any instructions for this evening?'

'Just to enjoy yourself.'

'And are those your plans, too?' He raised his glass with a cool smile and a slow flush darkened her cheekbones.

Adam took the untouched drink from her hand. 'You shouldn't be allowed out, my lady. Come on, let's go.'

The cocktail party was just another version of dozens she had been to. No better, no worse. But the commercial secretary, Mark Stringer, and his wife Angela were good company afterwards.

'What are you doing on Friday?' Angela asked.

'We've nothing planned,' Adam said. 'To be honest I had hoped to get away on the Friday flight, but Hanna is dragging everything out. He enjoys the haggling too much to be hurried.' He glanced briefly at Tara. 'At least I hope that's why he's delaying.'

'We're going to the races at Awali.' She turned to Tara. 'It's a long way from Ascot, but it's fun. Horses and camels. Why don't you come along?'

Tara made no response; it wasn't her place to accept such invitations. But Adam shrugged. 'Why not?'

They made the arrangements and then Adam drove Tara back to the villa. When they arrived there was a message waiting. 'Damn!'

'What is it?'

'The Ruler is holding a *majlis* tomorrow morning and I've been summoned to meet him.'

'A *majlis*?' Tara repeated. 'What is that?'

'It's a sort of open house. Anyone can visit the Ruler's *majlis* — his court, I suppose — and ask for favours, or for help, or just to pay his respects. Occasionally he holds formal ones, simply to shake hands with everyone. A bit like a Palace garden party, except it's less likely to rain and women aren't allowed. I have to go and shake hands with him.'

'Heavens, I'm impressed.'

He pulled a face. 'It will take all morning. You'll be bored to death here by yourself. I'll ring up Angela and ask her to take you down to the souk to do some shopping if you like. The gold shops are worth a visit.'

'There's no need.'

Adam's eyes narrowed. 'It's no trouble,' he said, firmly. 'And Angela will enjoy it.'

★   ★   ★

But half an hour before Angela was due to arrive she telephoned.

'Tara? I have a crisis. My youngest has broken out in a rash and I'm afraid it will need a trip to the doctor. I am so sorry.'

Tara was all sympathetic concern.

'Please don't worry, Angela. I'm fine here. I just hope there's nothing seriously wrong.'

'I have the disconcerting feeling that it might be chicken-pox. If so I shall have to go into purdah for a week or two.'

'Oh, I am sorry.'

'A mixed blessing, my dear. At least I won't have to host the bridge club this week. But I'm sorry to miss seeing you again.'

Tara wandered about the house for a while. She tidied up the office, glanced at a magazine and was wondering whether it was quite warm enough to put on her swimsuit and sunbathe in the garden when she heard a car arrive and the servant admitted Hanna Rashid.

'Tara, my dear,' he said, coming towards her, hands outstretched to take hers. 'Adam has left you here alone?'

'He's gone to the Ruler's *majlis*.'

'But of course. He mentioned it when we met yesterday.' He was still holding her hands and she pulled them free a little self-consciously. 'I have a little business with my staff and then I will give myself the inordinate pleasure of taking you out and showing you a little of the island.'

'I don't think — '

'Did you know that Bahrain is reputed to be the site of the legendary Dilmun? The lost Garden of Eden?'

Startled, not quite able to marry the place she had seen with her idea of Eden, she queried this statement.

'Certainly. There are ancient sites. We will visit them but you should perhaps change into something more comfortable.' His arm was around her shoulders and he was walking her to the stairs.

'No, really.' She turned quickly and freed herself. 'Thank you for your offer, but I should stay here.'

'You are too conscientious. Adam does not deserve you. The least he could do is organise a little entertainment while he is away.'

'Oh, he did,' she said quickly, and explained about Angela.

He was sympathetic. 'But then there is no reason why you should not take advantage of my offer. Adam clearly did not wish you stay here on your own and there may not be another opportunity to see a little of the island.'

He was right and despite Adam's dire predictions Hanna had behaved like a gentleman when he had escorted her home. Rather more so than Adam, she thought a little dourly. She glanced at her watch. It was still early and it would be wonderful to get out for an hour or two. 'Very well. But I must be back by one o'clock.'

'Whatever you wish,' he assured her easily.

She changed into a pair of navy cotton trousers and a silk jersey polo shirt in a vivid shade of fuchsia-pink. She had a pair of rope-soled shoes and slipped into those and grabbed a scarf.

As an afterthought she decided to leave a message for Adam. She paused for a moment over the little pad of stick-on notes. Then she was seized by a sense of devilment. 'Gone to discover the Garden of Eden with Hanna. Back by one. Tara,' she wrote. And she tacked it on to his bedroom door on her way out.

5

Tara was delighted with the island. Some parts were barren desert, others lush oasis. First Hanna took her to see an oil well chugging away, the nodding donkey gaily painted to look like a grasshopper.

'It's not at all what I expected. It's so small. So undramatic.'

'You are thinking of drilling rigs, *chérie*. They cost money. This makes it!'

He pointed out the palace where Adam was visiting the Ruler.

'Are you Bahraini?' Tara asked him. 'You don't wear the traditional robes.'

A shadow crossed his face. 'Bahrain is my adopted home. I am Lebanese.' He shrugged. 'One day I may go back.'

'I'm sorry.'

'There is no need to be. Come and look at the beach. It isn't warm enough to swim, but it is charming.' He parked the car and led her through deserted palm groves and gardens to a small beach, his arm lingering at her waist. 'The name Bahrain means 'two seas'. Here you see the salt water of the Gulf, but far below are freshwater springs that bubble up through the sea-floor. It is possible to dive down and capture it in a plastic bag.'

'So the salt sea overlies a freshwater sea?'

He was delighted that she understood. 'It is part of the legend of Dilmun.'

'You said there were ancient sites? Is this really the Garden of Eden?'

His smile was enigmatic. 'That you must judge for yourself. Come, I have arranged a small lunch.' He indicated a small pavilion set amid the palm trees and alarm bells began to ring in her head.

'Lunch?' She glanced at her watch. 'Good lord, it's nearly one o'clock. I have to get back.'

He laughed softly. 'Darling, you must

allow yourself to relax a little.' His hand at her waist compelled her gently towards the pavilion.

She dug her heels in. 'I'm afraid that's impossible, Hanna. Adam will be worried if I'm not back.'

'But you said he arranged for you to shop in the souk? He will simply assume you have decided to lunch out with Angela.'

'He would have,' she said, gently. 'But I left him a note saying that I was spending the morning with you.'

If he was annoyed he didn't let it show. Hanna's face betrayed only sadness. 'I did not realise. I did not see you enter the office.' And if he had, would the note have disappeared? She dispelled the idea as unjust.

'I left it upstairs.'

'Ah. In that case I must take you back. It would not do for him to come and find us alone together here. He can be so . . . ' he allowed a smile to cross his face ' . . . so puritanical.'

'Would he come looking for me?' she

146

asked, with well simulated surprise.

'Oh, yes, Tara. I'm very much afraid he would.'

'In that case I don't think we should delay. Thank you for the tour, Hanna.' She turned back to the car, detaching herself from his hand and adding a briskness to her voice. 'It has been most interesting.'

She quickly fastened the seatbelt before he decided to help. Adam had been right and she silently thanked whatever good angel had prompted her to leave a note. She wasn't certain Hanna believed her, but evidently he wasn't prepared to take the risk. And something that had been niggling at her all morning finally clicked into place. Hanna said that Adam had told him about the summons to the palace. But that was impossible because Adam hadn't known. She glanced across at her guide. Somehow she didn't believe it had come as a total surprise to the very smooth Mr Rashid.

Adam was standing in the doorway

when they drew up in front of the villa. Tara's heart sank slightly, she had almost hoped he would still be at the palace, but the way things were going it was inevitable that he should be home first.

'Did you have a good time?' he asked, without apparent rancour, and she began to relax. Then he turned to her and she saw his eyes. 'Did you find what you were looking for?'

'The Garden of Eden? I don't think so.' He might have been right about Hanna, but she wasn't about to give him the satisfaction of saying so. 'But it was most interesting.' She turned quite deliberately and offered the man her hand. 'Thank you for taking so much trouble to amuse me.'

'It was no trouble,' he assured her, bowing slightly. 'Another time we will explore at more leisure, *chérie*.' His eyes suggested he had more than ruins in mind.

'I look forward to it,' she said, somewhat recklessly.

'There are some telexes requiring answers, if you could spare a moment,' Adam said curtly. 'Hanna, can I offer you a drink?'

But Hanna Rashid apparently decided not to outstay his welcome as Adam joined her in the office almost immediately. 'How did you manage to shake off Angela?' he demanded.

She looked up from the telex keyboard. 'It wasn't necessary. Angela cancelled.'

'You're lying! I could see last night that you weren't keen on a trip to the souk. Now I know why. Hanna organised my 'invitation' to the *majlis* because you had already arranged this morning's jaunt.' His mouth was an angry slit. 'Where did he take you? His little beach pavilion?'

'He took me sightseeing, Adam.' Her hand shook slightly as she pressed the send button. 'I told you he was the perfect gentleman, and that is exactly how he behaved.' She might easily have imagined the sexual undercurrent in his luncheon invitation. But Adam's guess about the beach pavilion would seem to confirm it.

His eyes narrowed. 'I almost believe you. I wonder why?'

'Maybe because I'm telling the truth,' she said, crossly.

He shook his head. 'No. I wonder why Hanna is taking so long over your seduction?' He ignored her furious denial. 'One look is normally enough to have women eating out of his hand. When I discovered you had left the nightclub with him I was certain . . . '

'That he would bring me back here, flaunt his conquest under your very nose?' she asked, astounded.

'He naturally assumed that I have designs upon you myself. It would amuse him to cut me out.'

'Oh, I see! It's just a silly boys' game. You should have explained. I'll be a little nicer to him in future,' she added, the sugar-sweetness of her voice not disguising the angry sparkle in her eyes. 'If you'll excuse me I think I'll take a shower before lunch.'

'Tara?' She turned. His face was creased in a puzzled frown. He shook his head. 'Nothing.'

Lunch was a quiet meal. They were served a fine-fleshed white fish lightly coated in a prawn sauce and a green salad. Adam said very little, but once when she looked up, she caught him looking at her speculatively. She looked quickly away, but felt his eyes return to her again and again as if searching for an answer.

He spent the afternoon making phone calls, suggesting that she might like to rest before the evening.

'It's a formal party this evening, Tara. You did bring a long dress?'

'Yes, I brought a long dress with me.' And a certain satisfaction flickered through her veins. She was glad her safe black dress was hanging thousands of miles away where she couldn't be tempted to wear it.

But examining her reflection in the long mirror later that evening, she felt an altogether different sensation. She had made up to emphasise her dark eyes and painted her mouth scarlet to match her dress. Her black hair hung in a glossy curve to her naked shoulders and she had fastened long gold drops to her ears. Her throat she left bare. The fair flawless skin of her neck, her shoulders, her arms were all innocent of adornment.

The dress was simple in the extreme. A tiny bodice that hugged her figure, skimming lightly over her breasts and emphasising her narrow waist. The skirt, full, soft, brilliant, hung to her ankles. She had seen it in the window of a small boutique marked down in the January sales. She had always loved the colour and she'd had the money her godmother had sent for Christmas with the instruction that she buy something completely impractical. The dress had matched the description and she had bought it. But this was the first time she had worn it. It was stunning. She knew it and it frightened her, but it was too late for regrets. She lingered in her room until a tap at the door startled her into life.

'Are you ready, Tara?' Adam's voice from the other side of the door sent her heart hammering up into her throat. For a crazy moment she considered pleading a headache, sickness, possibly even insanity.

'I'll be down in a moment.' She picked up her tiny matching bag and a black wrap and with a last desperate glance at her reflection left the security of her room.

Adam was standing in the entrance hall, glancing impatiently at his watch when the movement from the stairs caught his attention.

He looked up and for a brief unguarded moment she saw a flare of desire heat the green eyes and her blood quickened in urgent response. Then the look was gone and she might have simply imagined it, it might simply have been a trick of the light, because his mouth was a straight hard line and his eyes held not the faintest gleam of warmth.

He had turned away and opened the door. 'I think I prefer you in the armour plating, Mrs Lambert. You keep better time.'

She fizzed with anger and she was still bubbling with it when Hanna welcomed them both to his luxurious town house. He at least knew how to compliment a woman and lost no time in doing so.

He took her hands in his and kissed them both. 'How beautiful you look tonight, Tara.' She felt Adam stiffen at her side and was glad.

'Thank you, Hanna.' She offered him her warmest smile and allowed herself to be drawn into the room and a glass of champagne placed in her hand. She raised it to him. 'Your good health,' she offered, knowing that Adam could hear every word.

'That is in your hands, beautiful *madame*. Where you hold my heart.'

Tara glanced at him quickly, wondering if he was making fun of her, but he seemed perfectly serious. She sipped the champagne nervously. 'Won't you introduce me to some of your friends?'

'Of course.' He was immediately the perfect host and, although he claimed the first dance with her, he surrendered her then to Mark Stringer with good grace.

She suddenly felt a great deal safer. 'How's the invalid?' she asked.

'Chicken-pox confirmed,' he said, glumly. 'I was just explaining to Adam that Angela was confined to barracks.'

'Oh, I am sorry. Send her my condolences.'

He nodded. 'I will.'

The evening moved headily on. Adam was apparently oblivious to her presence. Whenever she allowed her eyes to stray in his direction, he was deeply involved in conversation with one of the bankers present, or paying extravagant attention to one of the many beautiful women in the room. Only once did their eyes meet across the length of the room, then someone stepped between them and when she looked again he had disappeared. Not that she lacked attention herself. She had partners in abundance and Hanna was there to escort her into supper, attentive and charming, loading her plate from the buffet with foods strange and familiar. But after a while it all became rather cloying and she missed Adam's astringent conversation, but he was totally occupied with a fair beauty. Too much attention from Hanna Rashid, allied to the champagne, made her feel quite dizzy, and when he was distracted by someone else she took the opportunity to escape to the cool of the garden.

Tall French windows opened out on to a veranda and a flight of shallow steps led down to the path. The sound of splashing water drew her on into the darker part of the garden, until beyond the trees she saw a pool, lit by

submerged lamps with a curved dol-
phin that threw up a small fountain
from its spout. She stood for a moment
watching the water play against the
light. It was cooler than she had
expected and a shiver caught her by
surprise, making her wish she had
brought her wrap, but she was unwilling to return to the house and the
attentions of Hanna. She had tired of
the flirtation. If she had hoped to prick
Adam into some response she had been
singularly unsuccessful. Which was
perhaps as well.

She began to stroll about the garden
and in a few moments came upon a
little summer house half concealed by
bougainvillaea and scented herbs. There
was a huge sofa, loaded with soft
cushions, and she sank into it, grateful
to be away from the noise and clamour
of the party.

The first hint that she was not alone
was the soft plop of a champagne cork.

'It is a beautiful refuge from the
world, no?' Hampered by long skirts

and soft cushions, Tara tried to rise. But Hanna pressed a glass into her hand. 'This will revive you.'

'Will it?' she laughed a little nervously.

'I promise.' He bent and kissed the soft curve of her shoulder. Before she could register what he had done he was sitting beside her, but at least a foot away and it seemed churlish to protest. The man was a practised flirt; he would be congenitally incapable of resisting making a pass. Nevertheless, she wasn't about to encourage him further.

She looked around for somewhere to put her glass and he took it from her. 'Darling Tara. How clever of you to find my little pavilion.' He kissed her hands, then, without warning his mouth was blazing a trail along her arm. She tried to get up, but the sofa offered no resistance and he was leaning against her now, his weight pinning her back against the cushions.

'Hanna,' she protested, urgently.

'Yes, my darling. I'm here.' His

158

mouth was warm against her throat, his hand already cupping the soft mound of her breast. She began to struggle in earnest, but to no avail. She was sinking against the cushions, sliding down helplessly on to her back and he had thrown his leg across her.

She knew she would have to scream for help and the thought was sobering. The embarrassment would be acute enough in any circumstances, but Adam Blackmore's disdain would be unbearable. He had warned her. More than once.

Her protests were ignored and Hanna Rashid, having drunk altogether too much champagne, tugged roughly at her zip and exposed her breasts to the cool evening air. Now she was really frightened and in a panic lashed out, her nails raking his cheek. He swore, but didn't loosen his grip. Her struggles served only to excite him further and she opened her mouth. She no longer cared about embarrassment. 'Adam — ' It came out barely more than a croak. 'Ad — '

His hand clamped over her mouth '*Dieu*, Tara. But you are — ' What he thought of her was never to be known. Suddenly his weight was gone and she was left gasping for breath against the cushions.

The sound of a splash and angry stream of gutter French reached her from the pool and then Adam was there, breathing heavily, glaring down at her.

'Cover yourself up.' She stared at him, too stunned by the rapid succession of attack and rescue to move. 'Now!'

Tara struggled against the cushions and with a furious exclamation he reached down and yanked her to her feet and roughly pulled her dress into place, tugging up her zip so carelessly that he caught her flesh. She winced but made no sound. She didn't think he would be sympathetic to any pain she was suffering.

'I'm sorry, Adam.' She was shaking,

but he didn't seem to care.

'Not half as sorry as you're going to be.' He threw a savage glance at Hanna climbing disconsolately from the pool. Then without a word turned and hauled her after him up the steps of the veranda towards the house. Just before they reached the door he stopped so suddenly that they collided and he turned her into his arms. 'Now, Mrs Lambert, for once in your life do as you are told and co-operate.' Before she could ask what he meant he was kissing her. Kissing her with all the apparent passionate sincerity of a man bewitched. Only she knew it was all a lie, because once she had been kissed by him when he meant it.

Finally this humiliation was over and he released her.

'How dare you?' she breathed, furiously.

'Please don't think it gave me any pleasure, but far better, my lady, to have the assembled guests believe you were mussed up by someone you know, than a stranger you chose to flirt with despite all advice to the contrary.' He was breathing heavily. 'And this way no one will be surprised by our early departure.'

Tara was conscious of amused and knowing glances as they made their way to the door, Adam apparently determined to stop and bid farewell to every one of his many acquaintances. She bore it with as much grace as she could muster. What was a little embarrassment compared to attempted rape, after all?

But finally he allowed her to escape, dumping her unceremoniously in his car before striding around to the other door. 'What on earth possessed you?' he demanded.

'I just went out for a breath of air. He sort of leapt on me.'

'And you hadn't given him any encouragement, I suppose?' He started the car. 'My God, if that's how you led on that poor fool who was chasing you down Victoria Road I'm sorry I didn't leave you to his mercy. You could do with a lesson in sexual manners.'

She made no attempt to answer. Was too bitterly ashamed of herself to make any attempt to justify herself. She had flirted with Hanna Rashid simply to annoy Adam. But she could hardly tell him that. She sighed.

'I'm sorry, Adam. Have I completely ruined your business deal?'

'Don't flatter yourself. Money means more to Hanna than any woman.'

'But it will be awkward. You dumped him in the pool.'

'It was the quickest way I could think of to cool his ardour.' He scowled at her. 'And so much less undignified than a brawl.'

'But — '

'Don't fret, Tara. He'll have showered, changed and be flirting with some other female before we're back at the villa.'

She bit her lip. 'Will he?'

He glanced across at her. 'Yes. He's quite incorrigible. At least while his wife's away.'

This was the final straw. 'He didn't mention a wife, Adam, I — '

'Please don't pretend that it bothers you. I don't suppose you mentioned your husband, either.'

He pulled into the gates of the villa and Tara moved quickly, anxious to get away from him, get upstairs and out of her now hated scarlet dress.

'Don't go, Tara.' There was something in his voice that suggested disobedience would be foolhardy. 'I don't know about you, but I could do with a drink. A brandy?' He didn't wait for her reply, but poured two glasses and handed one to her. She didn't want it, but stood holding the glass, waiting to be read the riot act.

But Adam simply took off his jacket, pulled his tie loose and stretched out on a sofa. 'Come and sit down.' He patted the seat beside him.

'I don't think — '

'I'm not Hanna Rashid, my lady. I prefer my women to co-operate in their seduction.' She sat nervously on the edge of the sofa. 'To be fair to the man, he was short of time. He had to move quickly when you presented him with the opportunity.'

'I didn't . . . '

'That sofa is something else.'

She felt the colour drain from her face. He had clearly witnessed the whole thing. 'I tried to shout.'

'Yes. That's when I thought I'd better intervene. I promise I wouldn't have interrupted if I had thought you were enjoying yourself.'

'You . . . stood by and watched?'

'It's tough being a knight errant. Especially when the lady protests she can look after herself.' He drained his glass. 'It's a good job I didn't actually believe you. But then I do know Hanna of old. He didn't waste much time on the preliminaries, though, and that rather took me by surprise.'

Her cheeks flamed. 'I haven't thanked you for rescuing me,' she said, very quietly.

'No, you haven't.'

She glanced back at him. He was sitting in the corner of the sofa waiting for something more. 'Thank you.' She made a move to stand but he stopped her, taking her glass and placing it on a low table.

'That's not enough, Tara.' His eyes were hooded, concealing their expression, but there was a tenseness about him that boded nothing but trouble. Her emotions were already in turmoil; now, sitting so close to him, the scent of him was like a drug, making her skin vibrate, her pulse race. She wanted to run but she knew her legs wouldn't have carried her to the door.

'Adam — ' His name was only a breath on her lips.

His eyes never left hers as he took her fingers and raised them to his lips. 'Yes, Tara?' But she couldn't speak, mesmerised by the dark head bent over her arm, his lips gently exploring their way up the inner curve of her elbow, to the hollow of her shoulder. There was a yearning deep inside her. His touch bore no resemblance to anything she had felt before; he did not need to push her against the cushions. She opened to him like a flower, offering her throat, her eyes, her mouth to his teasing, delicate touch.

He outlined her lips with the tip of his tongue and her mouth parted gratefully, drinking in his kiss like a man dying of thirst in the desert.

They were the only two people left in the world and, lost to everything but him, she wound her arms about his neck. 'Love me, Adam,' she begged.

He raised his head and looked at her for a long, still moment. Then, almost regretfully, he shook his head.

'No. I don't think so.'

'What — ?'

He stood up abruptly and walked across to the drinks table, poured himself another brandy and drank it straight down. Shock held her pinned to the sofa. He turned back to her. 'That's it. The lesson is over. You can go now. But the next time you're tempted to start playing games, just remember how you're feeling now and have a little pity for your victim.'

It was a moment before she could move. Then she ran. She stumbled on the stairs, but managed to keep moving. Her hand trembled so much on the doorknob that she began to think it was locked, then it opened quite suddenly and she fell into the room. Tara slammed the door, turned the key and then ran for the bathroom.

She tore off her clothes, not caring what happened to them and stepped under the shower, scrubbing at herself until she tingled and her skin was pink. But it didn't take away the feel of his lips on her skin, or the pain.

She dressed in her pink pyjamas. She had always thought they were girlish, but he had said they were irresistible. She wondered what he would do if she went to his room right now. Resist like hell. He apparently found it easy.

She crawled miserably into bed, but couldn't sleep. She didn't even try. She was still trying to decide what on earth she could do to straighten out the mess she had made when the mournful cry of the muezzin from a distant mosque, calling the faithful to prayer, heralded the dawn. The sky lightened in the east and she was able to decently rise and dress to face the day, however painful it was likely to be.

She pulled on a pair of trousers and a light sweater and ran downstairs. She would have liked to walk, hard and fast, or swim, do anything to burn off the nervous energy that had pumped through her veins all night. All she could do was walk around the garden where she felt caged, shut in.

The manservant brought her a tray of tea and that made her feel a little better. Then she went into the office. Several telexes had arrived during the night and she sorted them and left them on Adam's desk for his attention. She checked the diary. Pointless, unnecessary tasks. But there was still no sign of Adam and distanced from the routine of an office she had nothing to do.

She ate breakfast alone. It should have been a relief, but it wasn't. She considered going up to see if he was all right. He wasn't the kind of man who lay in bed in the morning. Not by himself, anyway, she thought, and then wished she hadn't.

The telephone rang finally, making her jump, but at least it was something to do.

'Adam Blackmore's office,' she said, with a crispness she was far from feeling.

'Is that Tara?' The voice was that of a young woman, gentle, friendly.

'This is Tara Lambert,' she confirmed.

'I'm so glad to speak to you. This is Jane Townsend. Adam's — '

'Yes, of course,' she said, quickly. 'I'm afraid Adam's . . . not here at the moment.'

'Friday morning, I should have guessed.' The laughter was indulgent. 'He always overdoes it at Hanna's parties.'

'Does he?' Was that appalling hurt jealousy? Could she really be jealous that this woman knew how he behaved at parties? She closed her eyes in shame, sure that Jane would hear it in her voice.

But apparently she hadn't. 'Watch out for that man, Tara, he's a menace. But I expect Adam warned you.' There was such unreserved charm that Tara found herself warming to the owner of the voice, despite every desire to hate her.

'Yes, he warned me.' She couldn't say she hadn't been warned. It was her own fault she hadn't listened. 'Can I give Adam a message?' she asked, somewhat hesitantly.

'Yes, tell him I hope his hangover is hell.' She chuckled. 'And tell him that the clinic have decided to deliver the baby on Monday by Caesarian section.'

Her rush of sympathy was genuine enough. 'I'm sorry. Are there problems?'

'They've decided the placenta is in

the wrong place. I've been in and out of hospital for the last few weeks. Not allowed to touch my feet to the ground. It's been hell.'

'I can imagine.'

'Well, it'll soon be over. But I could do with some moral support, if he could manage to get back in time.'

Tara swallowed hard, furious that Jane even had to ask. 'Don't worry, I'll get him back in time if he has to swim.'

She shouted with laughter. 'Priceless. I do believe he's met his match at last. I can't wait to meet you, Tara.'

Tara hung up and when she turned Adam was standing in the doorway wrapped only in a towelling bathrobe. He looked dreadful. Unshaven and decidedly hungover. If she could have felt any joy at all, in would be in the fact that he clearly felt considerably worse than she did, at least physically.

He rubbed his chin with the palm of his hand and apparently did not much like the result. 'Who was that on telephone?'

'It was Jane.' She gave him the message and he swore softly.

'Timing never was her strong point. You'd better get us on the next flight out of here.' Tara turned quickly away. How on earth could he be so unfeeling?

'What about the meetings organised for tomorrow? Shall I cancel?'

'No, leave it to me. Get me Rashid on the phone now. And don't take no for an answer.' His mouth tightened. 'The one advantage of last night's little fiasco is that he will agree to almost anything. All I have to do is mention his wife's name.'

Her eyes widened in horror. 'You wouldn't — '

'Watch me.' He frowned at her distress. 'You don't owe him any favours, Tara.'

'I . . . '

'Yes?'

Her eyes dropped to her hands, busily shredding a tissue. 'I was partly to blame. You warned me.'

'Yes, I did. But you said no. He

didn't like it and considering the way you'd been flirting with him all evening I have some sympathy. But no still means no.'

'But to blackmail him . . . '

He made an abrupt move towards her, but stopped as she flinched away. 'Don't worry, Tara. All I want to do is speed things up. I shan't be too unkind. Just rob him of the fun of haggling down to the last cent.' His mouth twisted in a smile of pure derision. 'It will be more painful for him than being ducked in a fountain, I can assure you. And it won't cost him money.' He rubbed his forehead vigorously with his fingers. 'Well, not too much. Get Rashid, arrange the flight then bring your book up. I want the agreement in my hand for him to sign the minute he walks through the door.' He turned in the doorway. 'And I'd like some coffee if it's not too much trouble,' he added, caustically.

'And perhaps something for your headache?' she threw after him.

He bowed slightly in acknowledgement that her barb had found its mark. 'Thank you, my lady. That would be most appreciated.'

She put Rashid through to the bedroom phone. She had been nervous of speaking to him, but last night might never have happened. The call was brief and she was able to make the travel arrangements as soon as she had finished. That done she added her notebook and pencils to the tray brought by the servant and carried it upstairs.

His door was ajar, but she still knocked.

'Come in, Tara.' She pushed the door open, but the room was empty. 'I'm in the bathroom.'

'Oh!'

'Don't be a prude, girl. Get in here.'

Hardly knowing where to look, she peered around the door. He was lying up to his neck in a deep foaming bath, eyes apparently closed. 'Don't hover. Sit down and give me the painkillers.'

She handed him the tablets and a glass of water and he swallowed them.

Her own bathroom was beautiful, with a soft carpet and hand-made Spanish tiles, but Adam's was palatial. The bath was enormous, quite large enough for two. She squashed the thought hard. He had probably shared it with Jane on his last visit.

'Why are you blushing, Tara?'

'I'm sorry. I've never taken dictation from a man in his bath before.'

He opened one eye and eased up slightly, so that his shoulders appeared above the water. 'Would you rather I got out?'

'No!' She quickly sat in a comfortable wicker chair and stared down at her notebook.

He dictated more slowly than usual, clearly thinking about every word he used, weighing it, carefully. He asked her to read back what he had dictated more than once. He made several changes but was finally happy. 'That should do it. Knock it out as quickly as you can, Tara. And hand me that towel, will you?' He erupted from the water. She flung the towel at him and fled, pursued along the corridor by his laughter. He had clearly made a quick recovery.

She typed the document as quickly as she could, but kept making uncharacteristic errors as the image of his hard, well-muscled shoulders and the strong column of his neck kept intruding between her and the screen. She had printed it three times before she was satisfied. Adam appeared, casually dressed, ready for the journey and read it through. 'Fine.' He glanced at his watch. 'I'll print the rest of the copies; you'd better go and pack your things.'

'Shall I pack for you?'

He stared at her for a moment. 'Yes, thank you.'

She was halfway up the stairs when the front door opened and Hanna's voice called an almost unbearably cheery greeting to Adam. In that instance she knew what he had done.

He must have known how much she was dreading facing him and had got her out of the way. It was kinder than she deserved. She felt her throat tighten and knew she was close to tears.

'Stupid!' Tears wouldn't help. She blinked hard, but it was too late and as she swiftly folded her clothes into her case, small damp spots appeared with unhappy frequency. Finally everything was packed but the scarlet dress. She shook it out. It seemed pointless to pack it. She would certainly never wear it again. But she didn't know how to dispose of it and she could hardly leave it hanging in the wardrobe. With a sigh she folded it and lay it on top of her case and closed the lid.

Adam had already begun to pack his clothes. His shoes, his toiletries were already in the case. She emptied the wardrobe and drawers and did a neat workmanlike job, refusing the luxury of lingering over the crisp cotton of his shirts, the smooth silk of his ties. Only his dinner-jacket caused any problems.

It lay in a crumpled discarded heap behind the chair. She shook it out and was assaulted by his special scent, so evocative, so painful that she almost dropped it.

Falling in love, Beth had said, hurt. You wanted it to stop almost more than anything else. Except not stopping. She had thought she had loved Nigel. But what had she known about love? There had never been this dreadful ache, the longing to hold him, touch him. The pain in the knowledge that she must never touch him.

She and Nigel had been little more than children. Kissing, holding hands, never even . . . And then it had been too late. She tried desperately to conjure up his face, touching the little brooch he had made for her and which she had worn faithfully every day for him as if somehow it could conjure up the fragile past. But the only face that appeared to haunt her was Adam Blackmore. And Beth was right. It hurt.

6

They descended through the murk of low cloud into Heathrow, the grey day reflecting Tara's mood. At least they had been spared the silence of the outward journey. Adam had worked furiously on the new project all the way, waving away the food the stewardess offered without even asking if she was hungry. Not that she cared. Food would have choked her.

He kept up a steady stream of dictation until her wrist had ached and she had enough in her notebook to keep her totally occupied throughout Monday when Adam would be at the clinic. She would need it.

How she would get through the weekend was something else. But sleep seemed to deal with most of Saturday. She woke in the evening, wondering vaguely whether she had anything to eat in her tiny freezer. She opened the door, then closed it again.

But she had no bread and no milk. She had expected to be away until after the weekend or her neighbour would have taken some in for her. She made a dash through a wet evening to a nearby store owned and run by an extended family of Italians, which never seemed to close. The sharp clear air brought a touch of colour to her cheeks and she was greeted warmly, as an old friend.

It cheered her a little, and she decided that, hungry or not, she would make some scrambled eggs on toast before curling up in front of the television. She juggled the eggs and milk and loaf of bread as she struggled for her keys, finally managing to open the door without dropping anything. She had just put everything down in her tiny kitchen when there was a sharp rap at the door. She frowned. No one knew she was back so it couldn't be Beth. Besides, Beth wouldn't make that unholy racket.

Tara cautiously slid the chain across and opened the door a crack, letting out a startled scream as she saw the tall helmeted figure, night-stick at the ready.

'Come on out, miss. It's no good trying to escape.' The fierce creature had a voice to match his appearance but his expression was obscured by the visor of his helmet. She opened her mouth, but no sound came out. He moved a step closer.

She slammed the door. 'What do you want?' She tried to shout, but her voice was shaking too much.

'I'm from Maybridge Securities, miss,' he said, briskly. 'The occupant of this flat is away, so be a good girl and give yourself up. It'll save a lot of bother.'

She sagged against the door. Adam had said he would have her flat watched. She released the safety chain and opened the door. 'I'm sorry, but you gave me such a scare. I'm Tara Lambert.' He was unresponsive. 'This is my flat. We came back a few days early, Mr Blackmore . . . ' She had no need to explain. 'You can check direct with him. He's home.' Unless he was at the clinic with Jane.

The man seemed unimpressed. 'If you could just identify yourself?'

'I don't have to identify myself. I live here. I . . . ' Tara sighed. The man was simply doing his job, however unwelcome. 'Wait here.' She closed the door.

Whatever had happened to the smooth ordered existence that had been her life before Adam Blackmore had erupted into it?

The guard rapped on the door again. She was taking too long and he was getting suspicious. She fished her passport from her dressing-table drawer.

'Tara!'

Adam's voice on the other side of the door was the last straw. She flung it open and handed the passport to the security man. Adam took it from him.

'It's all right, Frank. You can leave it to me.'

'I'm sorry, Mr Blackmore, but the lady seemed to be fiddling with the lock . . . '

'Don't fret. You were just doing your job. Very well.'

'Right, Mr Blackmore.' He seemed relieved. 'I'll get off. Shall I keep up the patrols now the lady is home?'

'No,' Tara intervened quickly. 'Thank you.' Frank departed and before she could prevent him Adam was inside. She followed him and snatched her passport from his hand. 'Still hell-bent on your knight errant act?' Tara asked, angrily. 'You'll be trading in that black monster of yours for something white at this rate.'

'Any time, my lady.' He bowed ironically. 'Knight Errant Unlimited. And you already know my fee,' he drawled. 'One kiss, to be collected at my convenience.'

Her face whitened and he was immediately all concern. 'Oh, lord, I'm sorry. That must have been unpleasant. I should have let them know you were back, but to be honest when I got back from the clinic I just crashed out.'

He rubbed at his stubbly chin a little ruefully and Tara softened.

'You'd better sit down.'

He looked around. 'I like this. It's very pretty. Have you lived here long?'

'Nearly seven years. I moved in when they finished the conversion.' He ignored her invitation to sit down, but wandered around, examining the beams. 'These *are* genuine. When I saw them the other night I assumed they were just fakes.'

'Like you, Adam, I have no time for fakes.' She wished he would go, but he apparently had no intention of leaving. 'Would you like a cup of . . . ?' She stopped, self-consciously.

'I'd love a cup of coffee,' he said, gently. He followed her into the tiny kitchen alcove and spotted the eggs. 'Frank interrupted your supper.'

'Nothing special. I was just going to scramble some eggs.' She hesitated. 'Would you like some?'

He grinned. 'I thought you'd never ask.'

A few minutes later they were sitting either side of a solid wooden table tucking into the melting eggs. Tara was very quiet, determined not to do or say anything provocative. She never wanted to be accused of being a tease again.

But Adam's face showed his concern. 'Are you all right, Tara?'

'I'm fine.'

'Frank was just doing his job. You might have been anyone.'

'I know. I'm all right . . . really.'

'No, you're not. You're as jumpy as a kitten.' He placed his hand over hers and she duly jumped. He withdrew it quickly. 'Oh, I see. It isn't Frank, it's me. Do you want me to go?' She looked up, pleadingly into his eyes. She wanted him to go. She wanted him to stay. She just wanted him, but he belonged to someone else. It was unbearable. But he misunderstood. 'You're expecting someone. I should have realised.' He stood up. 'Mr Lambert, perhaps?

Although he doesn't appear to spend much time here.' He caught sight of the photograph on the mantel and took it down for a closer look. 'Your wedding photograph.' His mouth twisted slightly. 'The bridegroom is rather under-dressed for the occasion by most standards.' He glanced up at her. 'Your wedding night must have been . . . interesting.'

The colour rose to her cheeks. 'He'd broken his leg.' Riding his motorcycle much too fast because he was late for the wedding rehearsal.

'And you were married in the hospital? A rush job, was it?'

'There were circumstances — '

He was examining the photograph closely. 'It's difficult to see because of the traction, but you don't appear to be — '

'I wasn't,' she finally snapped, taking the picture from him. She looked at it, looked at those two happy faces. 'I think you'd better go now, Adam.'

He made no move. 'You were both

very young. What were you? Eighteen? Nineteen?'

'Eighteen,' she murmured.

'Too young. How long did it last?'

'Not long.' No time at all, in fact. She replaced the photograph, very carefully. 'He died the night this photograph was taken.'

'Died? The day you were married?' He stared for a moment at the photograph as if trying to understand. 'I'm sorry, Tara. I had assumed you were parted, but this . . . ' He moved towards her as if to offer some comfort, but she knew that if he touched her she could not help herself. She stepped from his reach and walked quickly to the door.

'I'd like you to leave, Adam.' For a moment she thought he wouldn't go. Then he picked up his soft, well rubbed leather jacket and slung it over his shoulder. But in the doorway he paused and turned back to her. 'Seven years is a long time to be alone, Tara. He wouldn't have wanted it.'

'I prefer it that way.' At least she had, until Adam Blackmore had kissed her.

'No, Tara. You're a woman made for love. We both know it. Hanna saw it too.'

'Please, Adam . . .' she begged.

But he hadn't finished. 'Is it guilt? Is that why you blow hot and cold?' He was suddenly very angry. 'Living isn't a sin, Tara. Nor is loving.'

She knew that, but surely it was wrong to desire a man who belonged to someone else? 'Please! Just go!' She closed her eyes to blot out his face and when she opened them again, he had gone.

*   *   *

Sunday was bleak. She rang Beth to let her know that she was back but refused her invitation to lunch. One look at her gaunt, unslept in face and Beth would know what her friend was going through. She needed just a little time to put her mask back into place before she was prepared to face the world.

She went for a long walk along the river. There were already daffodils in the gardens on the opposite bank making a brave effort to cheer the greyness of the day. It might even have felt quite warm if she hadn't spent the last few days in a hotter climate.

But the wind whipped some colour into her cheeks and the exercise made her blood tingle with life. Until she met Adam Blackmore she had been happy. She told herself that she could be happy again. It would take a little time. But she had plenty of that.

★   ★   ★

But first she had to get through Monday. She woke heavy-headed, for once in her life unwilling to face the day. A shower helped and as she dressed, layering on her armour, she became stronger. She stared at her reflection in the mirror.

Her face was a little paler than usual,

her eyes darker. But apart from that there was nothing to betray the fact that the shell that had protected her heart for so long had been shattered and now it lay in her breast, bruised, battered, aching. She rested her hand lightly over the place. It continued to beat. Life went on. It was a lesson she had learned once and she would learn it again in time.

Work was the answer. If for a few weeks she was tied to her agreement with Adam Blackmore, so be it. She would cope. She would have to. At least the sun was shining, and Tara stepped out briskly, lifting her chin to the world, unaware of the admiring glances that her cool dark beauty attracted from men pausing momentarily in their own swift progress to watch her pass.

Tara took the main lift. Somehow the private lift seemed too personal, and she wanted to get her relationship with Adam back on to a strictly impersonal plane.

She was greeted with unexpected

warmth by the receptionist and several other staff members who crowded into the lift alongside her. They seemed to think she belonged. But she didn't. She was an outsider. A temporary secretary. That was the way she had always wanted it. Until she'd met Adam Blackmore.

She rode the last stage by herself to the private domain of Adam Blackmore. His office was empty, the desk immaculate as always. She hadn't expected him to be there, he would be at the clinic, pacing impatiently while Jane was in Theatre. She shook herself and went through to her own office.

Her own desk was, in stark contrast, piled up with post and messages. She took off her coat, filled the coffee-maker and set it to work. She had a feeling she would be needing it.

She gradually worked through the pile, dealing with what she could by herself and answering queries. Then she set herself to clear the work that Adam had dictated on the journey back from Bahrain.

It was late when she printed off the last memo and she was tidying her desk, leaving everything straight for the morning when she heard the lift arrive.

She prayed that he would go straight into his apartment, or even his office, giving her a chance to escape without speaking to him, but to no avail.

Her door opened. 'Still here?' he asked. 'I thought you would have left hours ago.'

He looked tired and a pang of sympathy wrenched at her. She wanted to ease the tie from his neck, stroke the furrows from his forehead, kiss away the strain. 'I wanted to finish everything.'

'Of course,' he said, dully. 'Little miss perfect.'

Stung, she asked, 'How is Jane?' She had to keep jabbing at the hurt, reminding herself that what she felt for this man was foolish nonsense.

'Jane?' He rubbed his hand over his face. 'Oh, she's fine. So is Charles Adam Townsend, thank heavens.'

'Congratulations.' Her voice sounded

quite normal she thought as she straightened her desk once more.

'What?' He shrugged. 'Oh, right. I'll pass it on to the appropriate quarters. If you've finished you'd better get home.'

'Yes. I've left a list of messages on your desk, but I'll fill you in tomorrow.' It wasn't so difficult if you kept to safe subjects, she thought.

'Not tomorrow. Not ever.' Shock lifted her head and she was confronted by his emotionless face. 'I don't want you to come back, Tara.'

Why was she surprised? She hadn't behaved much like the perfect secretary during the last few days. He was at her side in a stride. 'Don't look at me like that, damn you. I'll keep to our agreement. If your temps are half as good as you I'll have the better part of the bargain.' He stepped back, clearly regretting the impulse that had brought them within inches of each other. He waved her away. 'I've kept you from your own affairs long enough. Just get me someone here tomorrow who can type.'

'Until Jane comes back?'

His mouth tightened. 'Jane won't be coming back.'

Of course not. She could hardly deposit the boss's son in the fifth-floor crèche every morning. Tara had been conscious of the dull ache in her chest all day, but now it threatened to explode. She clenched her hands. Keep to business. Think of business and it would be all right.

'Would you like me to look for a new secretary for you?' she asked, with every evidence of being completely calm. Completely in control. This seemed to anger him.

'Yes. Just make sure she's middle-aged and plain and wears flannelette underwear.'

Tara's cheeks flamed. 'I'll keep those requirements in mind, Adam, but frankly, I prefer to make my judgements on skill and personality.'

'Do you? Well, to be honest I don't care overmuch whether she can even

195

type, Tara. Just so long as she doesn't answer back!'

There were tears burning against her lids now and she had to get out before they began to fall. She grabbed blindly for her bag and her coat. 'I'll bring someone in the morning. Walk them through the system.'

'No. You managed. So must she. I don't want you here.' He caught her arm and swung her to face him. 'Have I made myself clear?'

'Let go of me!'

He looked down at his hand on her arm, as if wondering how on earth it had got there. Then his eyes flashed up into hers.

'I'll let go in my own good time.'

'Adam!'

'Before you go you'll have to settle your outstanding obligations.'

'I have no obligations to you — '

'Your outstanding fee for services rendered.'

'What — ?'

He drew her slowly towards him. She

was shaking her head, pulling desperately in her need to get away. But there was no escape. His eyes fastened her to the spot like a butterfly on a pin. Barely conscious that he had released her, she still could not turn and run.

He took her bag and coat from her lifeless fingers then, his hands at her waist, warm, strong, electric through the smooth cloth of her jacket, he drew her towards him. His mouth was closer now. Descending slowly, as if he didn't want the moment to pass. Slowly, drawing her body along the length of his. Slowly, while he drank in every feature as if for last time. His lips touched her forehead, her brows, gently caressed her eyelids.

Tara moaned as if in mortal agony, but his mouth was relentless in its soft seduction. It courted her temples, wooed the strong curve of her jaw and the delicate, sensitive skin below her chin. The touch of his lips to hers was both a relief and a menace. Somewhere, deep inside, she knew she should be fighting for her survival. There was some good reason why she should fight this seductive pleasure. But her body wasn't listening.

Softly his lips moved across hers, tempting, flirting, drawing from her little whimpers and moans of longing that she wasn't even aware of. His tongue flickered teasingly and her lips parted in welcome. This was the kiss she had waited for all her life. Nothing had ever prepared her for the singing sensation, the glorious power she felt surging through her. Nigel had never made her feel remotely like this. Nigel . . .

She wrenched herself free and fell back against the desk. What on earth was she doing? A few minutes ago this man had said he never wanted to see her again. He was simply extracting payment for a totally imaginary good deed.

'Tara!' He reached for her to help her to her feet, but she rejected him.

'That's enough!' She straightened,

drawing herself to her full height. Not enough. Not nearly enough, but it seemed to have the desired effect. Adam stepped back. 'I'm afraid you'll have to consider your fee paid in full, Adam.' She fumbled in her bag. 'Here's the key to your private lift. I shan't be needing it again.' She flung it on the desk, pushed past him and ran.

She tried the button to summon the main lift. But the door opened behind her and she would not wait. She fled to the stairs and began to run helter-skelter down them. She had to get away whatever it took.

She reached the ground floor gasping, almost retching. And still she had not escaped. He was there, swearing softly as he lifted her, carried her to his car. She couldn't speak. Couldn't scream that she just wanted to be left alone. But the grim cut of his face was a warning that it would make no difference. He was in no mood to listen.

They reached her flat in a few moments and once more he was at her side before she could move. The pain in her chest was beginning to subside, but she hadn't the strength to push him away when he lifted her from the car and carried her up the steps.

'Open the door, Tara.' She opened her bag with shaking fingers and found her keys, jabbing desperately at the lock until it slid home and the door swung open. He carried her through without a word and deposited her on the sofa.

She heard the sound of water running and then he was handing her a glass of water. 'Sip this.' She did as she was told. He sat for a while in the chair opposite, saying nothing, elbows on his knees, his head slumped forward, simply waiting until she had recovered sufficiently to sit up. Then he stood up and left, quietly closing the door behind him.

She heard the car start and drive away and then for a long time there was nothing but silence.

★　★　★

Beth exclaimed with delight when she opened the office door and found Tara already at work.

'Hello, early bird. You're a sight for sore eyes! I've been rushed off my feet.' She chattered on about the sudden upturn in business as she plugged in the coffee-maker. 'I don't know what you did for the gorgeous Mr Blackmore, but we've placed two senior secretaries at Victoria House and I'm looking for a permanent junior. Do you know anyone?' She didn't wait for a reply. 'And I'm going to see Jenny on Thursday about getting some computer staff in there.'

'Just be sure to get off the lift at the right floor,' Tara advised, cryptically, without looking up from the file. 'There are one or two girls I've interviewed recently who might do. And I've sent Mary Ogden to work for Adam while I find someone permanent for him.'

'Mary?' Beth said doubtfully. 'She's very good, of course, but I wouldn't have thought she was quite his style.'

Tara considered the starchy fifty-year-old. 'On the contrary, although I can't guarantee she fulfils every one of his stringent requirements, I believe she will suit him admirably.'

Beth gave her a long look, then shrugged. 'You know your business, I suppose, and you've worked for the man. What was the overseas trip like?' Tara finally raised her head and Beth smothered a gasp as she saw the painful shadows beneath her friend's eyes. She started to say something, but changed her mind and forced a laugh instead. 'Perhaps Mary is a good idea after all.' She busied herself with her post and the day's work began.

If Beth noticed that Tara was tense as a spring, jumping every time the telephone rang, she made no comment. Gradually though, as the day wore on and she became more deeply immersed in following up the opportunities for work for her girls, Tara began to uncoil. Once or twice she caught Beth looking at her sympathetically. It had a bracing effect, straightening her back, reminding her to paint the smile back on her face.

'I'm just going to get some sandwiches for lunch,' Beth said suddenly, at about twelve.

Tara didn't look up from the telephone directory. 'Fine. Get me — ' But Beth hadn't waited to hear what she wanted. The door closed with a bang. Tara looked up, exasperated. 'Well, thanks . . . ' The words died on her lips as she saw Adam standing in the doorway.

'I believe that is what is known as a strategic withdrawal.' He flicked the lock up.

'What do you want, Adam?'

'Is that any way to greet someone bearing gifts?'

'I don't want any gifts from you.'

He perched on the edge of her desk, not in the least put out by the sharpness of her tongue. 'But this isn't from me.' He produced a small box from his pocket and an envelope. 'It came by courier this morning. All the way from Bahrain.'

He handed her the small leather covered jeweller's box. She looked up at him, puzzled. 'What is this?'

It was his turn to be sharp. 'Open it and see.'

She pressed the catch. On the bed of velvet nestled a pair of creamy pearl ear studs. 'Oh, how beautiful.' He took the box from her hand and examined the contents.

'Yes. A pair of pearls, matched for colour and size. Quite exquisite. From the Bahrain pearl-beds, of course.' He regarded her with wintry eyes. 'Hanna has excellent taste. They will suit you perfectly.' He handed them back to her. 'Try them on.'

'Hanna sent them for me?'

'The letter was sealed, but I took an educated guess. Who else could it be?'

'You didn't steam it open to make certain?' She snapped the box shut. 'I don't want his letter and I don't want his pearls. Send them back.'

His lip curled slightly. 'There's no need to be so dramatic. It's simply his way of apologising.'

'I don't need his apology. As you took so much trouble to point out, I had no one but myself to blame for what happened. Send them back,' she repeated, stubbornly.

'I can't do that, Tara. If I send them back he will simply assume that I never gave them to you.'

'And that matters to you?'

'I may have mixed feelings about the man, but he is a brilliant money broker. For the moment we are partners in raising funds for my latest project.'

'I'm afraid that's your problem. I don't want them.'

He smiled slightly and stood up. 'You could always sell them. The money would make quite a dent in your overdraft.'

'What do you know about my overdraft?' she demanded.

'I didn't know anything. But your reaction tells me plenty.'

'Adam!' she protested, as he moved to leave. 'You can't leave these here.'

But he had already opened the door, carefully replacing the catch. 'Consider it a bonus, Tara. After all, you clearly earned it on your visit to the beach pavilion. I'm sorry I misunderstood the scene in the summer house. If I hadn't interrupted you would surely have had the necklace to match.'

She flung the stapler at his head but too late. He had already gone. It bounced harmlessly off the wall and fell to the floor.

Beth bent and picked it up as she returned, replacing it on the desk without comment. 'I bought you cream cheese and smoked salmon. You look as if you could do with a treat.'

'Bribery will get you nowhere, Beth Lawrence. How dare you skip out like that and leave me alone with him?'

Beth had the grace to blush. 'I'm sorry, but he didn't look as if he wanted an audience.'

Tara sighed. 'No. I don't suppose he

did.' She opened the envelope. There was a small certificate from the jeweller guaranteeing the authenticity of the pearls, and a note.

Hanna had been brief. 'Forgive me, beautiful Tara. I did not understand. Hanna.'

She picked up her pen and wrote simply, 'Forgiven. Tara.' Then she called an international courier service and sent it and the pearls back.

* * *

Mary Ogden, white-lipped and quivering with indigation, came into the office just after three the next day. 'I'm sorry, Tara. I did my best, but that man is impossible to work for.'

Tara's heart sank. 'You've left Mr Blackmore?'

'My ability has never been questioned before.'

'I'm sorry, Mary. I know he's not the easiest man in the world to work for and I — er — believe he has been under some strain recently. But I really thought you would have been able to cope.'

'Of course I could have coped. I simply asked him to slow down a little when he was dictating.' She assumed a look of injured dignity. 'He said his last secretary could keep up with him!' She made a noise that suggested no one could keep up with him. 'There's nothing wrong with my shorthand and I told him so.'

'And that's when he asked you to leave?'

'Not in so many words.' She compressed disapproving lips. 'He simply suggested that if I was having a problem keeping up with him I had better look for a less demanding job. I told him that I have worked for — '

Tara smothered a groan. 'Yes, Mary. Your experience is without question. Sit down and have a cup of coffee.' She soothed the ruffled feathers, promised to try and find her another job as quickly as possible and heaved a sigh of relief when she finally departed.

Beth chuckled. 'Do you think he's trying to tell you something?'

'What?' Tara snapped.

Beth raised her hands in surrender. 'Sorry. None of my business. What are you going to do now?'

'I'm not quite sure.' She reached for the telephone. 'But I'd better do something.' She made arrangements with another of her temps to take Mary's place.

'Don't you think you ought to have warned her?' Beth asked, when she replaced the receiver.

'No. It'll only make her nervous.' Beth looked sceptical as she dialled Adam's number and waited with growing trepidation for him to pick up the phone.

'Adam Blackmore,' he barked down the phone. Tara waited. 'Hello?' Marginally more friendly, she thought crossly. But not good enough. There was a pause, then a soft laugh that sent shivers down her spine. 'Hello, my lady. I wondered how long it would be before you phoned.'

7

Her grip on the telephone was painful. 'Good afternoon, Adam,' she said, crisply. 'I have reason to believe you need another secretary.'

'I do. And would it be too much to ask for one who can take down a few simple notes without having hysterics this time?'

'Mary has never had hysterics in her life,' she said, coldly. 'I don't understand your problem, Adam. She was exactly what you asked for. Even down to the underwear,' she added rashly, her fingers firmly crossed. 'With the added bonus that she can actually type.'

Beth's eyebrows were working overtime on the other side of the office, but Tara studiously ignored them, furiously wishing she hadn't allowed herself to say anything so stupid. The common sense she had always prided herself on appeared to have deserted her. She wondered if Adam Blackmore had stolen it, along with her heart.

'You remembered?' he asked, softly.

She swallowed. Of course she remembered. She would never forget anything he had said or done. She would never forget the way he had held her, his kiss that had driven every thought from her head, leaving only him to fill her mind, until the cold draught of sanity had dragged her back to reality.

'Tara?' he prompted.

'Of course I remembered,' she said, with all the outward appearance of calm. 'Nothing is too much for a client. Any client,' she added, and quickly continued. 'You can expect a suitably qualified senior secretary by the name of Lisa Martin at nine o'clock tomorrow morning.' He made no response to this and Tara was beginning to find it difficult to breathe. 'She is our very best shorthand secretary. She doesn't normally work during the school holidays, but I have managed to persuade her to work for you,' she rushed on. He ignored all this.

'I'm glad you have a good memory. It will help to keep you warm on cold winter nights.' His voice was without emotion, yet as he dropped the receiver back on to the cradle she shivered.

She put the phone down quickly and snatched her hand away as if somehow he could reach out through the receiver and hold her. She had tried to be businesslike, but he continued to torment her. Why? He was the one who said he didn't want to see her ever again. So why couldn't he just leave her to get on with her life?

What life? forlornly echoed back in her head. Before she had met Adam she had had her work. A new business to build up with Beth, a pleasant social life and a godmother in the Lake District who emerged only for weddings and funerals these days and whom she didn't see enough of, but whom she loved dearly.

She still had all those things, but

none of them seemed to matter very much. Perhaps if she had had a family, brothers and sisters it would have been different. But she had never known her parents. Mr and Mrs Lambert had taken her in when she was orphaned as a baby. She smiled. She had been lucky, she knew. They had cared for her as if she had been their daughter and she had always thought of Nigel as a nothing more than a big brother, until he'd gone away to college to study design.

She had missed him so much more than she had expected. Other girls seemed to quarrel endlessly with their brothers, but Nigel had always been there for her, protecting her, the very best friend she had ever had. When he'd asked her to marry him it had seemed so obvious, so right.

She sighed. There had been none of the searing, blazing passion that Adam generated by his very presence, by the sound of his voice on the telephone. Nigel hadn't turned her bones to jelly, her blood to fire. It had been a comfortable, easy relationship. They would have been happy, given the chance. But a small doubt niggled at the back of her mind. If she had met someone like Adam Blackmore, would it have been enough? Perhaps that was what Jane's marriage had been like. Comfortable. Until Adam Blackmore settled like a thorn under her skin.

The afternoon seemed to drag interminably. Despite work left on her desk, as soon as the clock turned five-thirty Tara pulled on her coat.

'What's the hurry?' Beth asked, surprised.

'I've had enough. I need a hot bath, a bowl of spaghetti and a very large bar of chocolate. In no particular order.'

Beth looked sympathetic. 'I recognise the symptoms. Go and wallow. You'll feel so guilty tomorrow that you won't have the time to worry about the heartache.'

Tara was going to deny it, but she realised in time that it would be

pointless. Beth was an incurable romantic, falling in and out of love at the drop
of a hat.

'Is it like this for long?' she asked.

'It varies, sweetheart. What was it like
when Nigel died?'

Tara tried to remember. 'It wasn't
like this, Beth. I grieved for Nigel. I
loved him. I'd loved him all my life.' She
shook her head. 'But it wasn't like this.'

Beth shook her head. 'If you'd like to
go away . . . you could do with a
break . . . '

'Perhaps later.'

'Look. Delay the bath. Come and
have the spaghetti at Alberto's with me.
We'll have some of that amazing
chocolate cake he does and a bottle of
Chianti. The very best sticking plaster
for a broken heart, I promise.' She
grinned. 'Trust me. You can fall into the
bath later.'

Tara suddenly laughed. 'You're right.
Come on. I can't wait.'

'Oh, well done.' Beth said, approv-
ingly. 'You're going to make an

excellent patient.'

Beth had her giggling through the meal, telling her the most outrageous stories about the many boyfriends she had had over the years. 'I don't believe it,' she finally protested. 'That's too much.'

Beth shrugged. 'Ah, well. It's my contention that you should never spoil a good story by sticking too precisely to the truth.'

When they parted in Victoria Road to go their separate ways, Tara felt better. The laughter had helped. She didn't think it would last, but tonight she would have a soak in the bath and she would sleep.

'Good evening, Mrs Lambert.' The security guard raised his hand in salute as she passed him.

She let herself in, her good mood evaporated in the space of a second. She glared at the telephone. She should ring him and tell him to call off his watchdog right now, but the morning would do. And she wouldn't telephone.

She would have to keep her distance from Adam if she was ever to recover her equilibrium. She would send him a polite little note instead.

The light on the answering machine was winking and she pressed the play button. There were a couple of calls from people she hadn't seen for a week or two. A message from Jim, sounding quite desperate, asking her to ring him. The last call was a voice she had heard before, but couldn't quite put a name to.

'Tara? I hope this is the right number, I got it out of the phone book. I wondered if you would come into the clinic and see me if you can spare the time? Perhaps at the weekend. Saturday at about four o'clock would be a good time.' Jane? 'Sorry, this is Jane Townsend. I should have said that first. I'm absolutely hopeless with these things. I'm rather worried about Adam and I think it's time we had a little chat.'

Oh, yes, it was Jane. That warm

breathless charm was unmistakable. And she wanted to have a little chat about Adam. Warn her off, more likely. Under the circumstances she would probably feel the same way. She angrily turned the taps on in the bathroom, her mood destroyed completely, wondering what friendly little voice at Victoria House had taken the trouble to pass on the information that she should watch her back.

Well, she would go. She owed the woman that. She would reassure Jane that she had no intention of disrupting her domestic arrangements with Adam. For her own peace of mind she hoped never to speak to the man again.

And Jim was back on her trail. It was time she put an end to that once and for all. She dialled his number but there was no reply. Then with a squeal of panic she fled to the bathroom just in time to prevent a flood.

★ ★ ★

She did sleep. She awoke heavy-eyed and heavy-limbed to the alarm clock, hardly sure what day it was. She lay still for a moment collecting her thoughts. Thursday. The week was apparently endless. But it was Thursday. Time to get up. Thursday was a busy day.

She climbed out of bed. The paperboy had pushed the local weekly through the letterbox and the postman had delivered his usual quota of bills. She picked them up and dumped them on the kitchen table and went and stood under the shower to finish waking up.

She checked her diary. There were several appointments which caused a frown to gently furrow her brow. She and Beth had to make up the salary cheques for the girls today for collection on Friday. And there was the local newspaper to scan for advertisements for vacancies and follow-up contacts to make offering to take the pain out of staff hunting.

She swallowed her tea, grabbed the

219

mail and newspaper and hurried to the office. It was only just past eight o'clock when she arrived, but Beth followed her in with the same idea of getting an early start.

They both settled down immediately to their respective newspaper advertisements and had a list to work through by nine-thirty. Beth did quite well, despatching a couple of her people for interviews, and then prepared to depart for her chat with Jenny Harmon.

'I can't wait to see the inside of Victoria House. The Atrium is lovely. Such gorgeous shops. So individual, not all carbon-copy replicas of every other shopping centre.'

Tara half smiled. They might not look it, but every one of them was part of a countrywide chain. Like the wine-bar, they were all part of the Blackmore empire. A very small part. But instead of working at an instantly identifiable image, each shop had been individually designed for its locality and given its own name. People, women who wouldn't have been seen dead in a chain-store used them every day without a qualm.

'The whole building is quite stunning. I'd love to be able to afford a suite there. People would have to take us rather more seriously if we could boast Victoria House as our address.'

'Hey, listen, lady,' Beth said, sternly. 'We are being taken seriously these days. Business is looking up and the holiday season hasn't started yet.'

'Yes, you're right.' And there was the added bonus of her fee for working for Adam. Financially at least, things were getting better, and not just because of Victoria House; word seemed to be getting around. 'It'll be all smiles at the bank next week.'

'Oh, it has been this week, my love. Quite a change of atmosphere. The manager actually spoke to me yesterday. Just to pass the time of day.'

'Wonders will never cease. Here we go.' The temps began the lunchtime rush with their time-sheets.

'I'll bring you back a sandwich.'

When Beth returned triumphant some time later, Tara took the opportunity to walk down by the river for a blow of fresh air. March had tipped over into April and suddenly it was warmer, more springlike, with blossoms everywhere. She sat on a bench watching the river. The leisurecraft were being moved into position for the summer season and there was a general bustle about which she would normally have loved to watch.

But nothing seemed to register. Tara watched it all happening as if she were seeing events taking place on a stage a long way off. Nothing seemed to involve her any more. She sighed and opened the newspaper and instantly her eye was drawn to a photograph of a young dark-haired woman, baby cradled at her elbow, a smiling man leaning over to touch the tiny fingers. Adam. The paper dropped from her lifeless fingers.

She had known, yet she had still

fallen in love with him. She hadn't believed such things happened. She had always imagined people were in control of their own destinies. If they were foolish and irresponsible they got hurt. But she hadn't wanted to fall in love. She had been content with her life. It hadn't been exciting, but she had friends, had her work and the challenge of the new business. Her life would go on, she supposed. Outwardly it would hardly change at all. But she knew that contentment had flown out of the door the night she had thrown herself, unwittingly, into Adam Blackmore's arms.

★　★　★

She finally moved, surprised to find how cold she was. She glanced at her watch. She had been sitting there for two hours. Guilt carried her back to the office on winged heels, her arrival coinciding with that of Lisa Martin, who pounced on her.

'I'm sorry, Tara. You'll have to find someone else for Mr Blackmore.'

Tara's heart sank. 'Oh, dear. Is it the children?' she asked hopefully. 'There is a crèche at Victoria House; maybe something could be arranged.'

'It's nothing to do with the children. It's him.'

Beth raised her eyes speakingly to the ceiling, then poured a cup of coffee and sat the woman down. 'Tell me about him,' she said. 'You're the third secretary he's had this week and I'm beginning to get interested. What did he do? Complain about your shorthand?'

Tara flashed a warning look at Beth. 'He does dictate very fast.'

'That's something of an understatement. I don't know who his last secretary was, but I suggested if she was that good he had better get her back no matter what it cost him.' She half frowned. 'He said that money wasn't the problem. I told him it wasn't a problem for me, either. I wasn't prepared to work for him at any price.'

Tara sighed. 'All right, Lisa. We'll pay you for today and tomorrow.'

When she had gone she and Beth exchanged a glance. 'It's deliberate, isn't it?' Tara asked. 'I'm not being paranoid?'

'It's deliberate. And off the top of my head I'd say Lisa has it about right. He wants you back. Although whether he knows it is a moot point.'

'He . . . ' Her voice quivered. She cleared her throat. 'Nonsense. Anyway, he can't have me. And if he keeps this up he won't have anyone.' She pulled a pile of time-sheets towards her.

'You're not going to telephone him?' Beth asked.

'No, I don't think so. If he wants someone, let him call us.'

'Going to make him beg?' Beth asked, slyly, with every appearance of innocence.

Tara shook her head. The thought of Adam Blackmore begging for anything was unimaginable.

The afternoon was devoted to the

payroll, which required careful concentration, and the phone was so busy that she soon forgot to jump every time it rang. It was a shock then to suddenly hear his voice, so close, against her ear.

There was no polite preamble. 'Tara. I've been waiting for your call.' She gripped the phone convulsively, quite unable to speak. 'You must know by now that I need another secretary.'

'Lisa did drop by on her way home. I'm afraid I shall have to invoice you for the full two days for her.'

'Find me a decent secretary,' he said, sharply, 'and we'll talk about it.' He hung up.

Tara stared at the phone for a moment, then replaced it on the receiver. 'Any ideas?' she asked Beth with a sigh.

'You know what I think.'

'You're wrong, Beth. He told me to go. That he didn't want to see me again.'

'Did he?' Beth considered. 'Then if you don't mind me saying so, he's going a funny way about it. Why don't you take pity on the man?'

Tara lowered her thick dark lashes to conceal the sudden brightness in her eyes. 'Beth, his last secretary has just had a baby. It's her I'm taking pity on.'

'Oh, my dear. I'm so sorry.'

'Please don't . . . ' But it was too late. The threatening tears spilled down her cheeks.

Beth busied herself with filing cards. 'How about Mo? Her shorthand is good.'

Tara shook her head. 'She doesn't deserve it. None of them does.'

'Got it! Janice is our girl!'

'But I thought she was working for the accountants on a permanent basis now.'

'She called in on Monday to say she's back in the market. She's unflappable, takes a hundred and fifty words a minute without flinching and she's not afraid to speak her mind.' She chuckled. 'It's the nearest he's going to get to you. Except in age.'

'I wonder what her underwear is like?'

'Tara?' Beth was looking at her a little oddly.

'Sorry, thinking out loud.'

'I see. Well, leave Janice to me. I think you should run along home. You look fit to drop.'

'You say the kindest things.'

Beth tilted an eyebrow at her. 'I suppose it's only polite to phone the man and let him know who to expect in the morning?'

'No.' Tara shook her head. 'Let him sweat.' She almost managed a smile.

★ ★ ★

Saturday dawned bright and clear. The first real warm spring day. Tara barely noticed. She cleaned her flat thoroughly, making sure her hands were occupied, but it didn't help her head or her heart. Today she would have to face Jane and reassure her that she had no competition, and was trying very hard not to think about it.

After lunch, a sandwich she barely touched, Tara went to change.

A plain grey skirt, an old but favourite white blouse from Laura Ashley, its collar fanned up like a ruff, a long black knitted edge-to-edge jacket. The barest touch of make-up. Her hair pulled back and tied with a neat red bow at the nape. She surveyed herself in the mirror. Jane would never believe she was a threat in such an outfit. She was so used to the fine bones, the elegant winged brows, the full mouth that were reflected in the mirror, that she was able to dismiss them as ordinary. She smiled at her reflection. She must remember to smile.

On the final few steps to the front of the clinic she almost lost her nerve. She could always write . . . or phone . . . anything but this.

A friendly porter made a point of coming over. 'First visit? Where do you want to go?'

'Maternity,' she almost croaked.

He pointed the way and stood and watched to make sure she followed his directions, nodding encouragement as she seemed to hesitate.

She found Jane's room with a little help from a nurse and tapped at the door.

'Come in.' The voice was instantly recognisable.

She opened the door and stepped inside. There was no turning back.

Jane Townsend looked at her curiously for a moment. 'Are you Tara Lambert?' she asked, with apparent surprise. Then her face widened in a smile. 'How kind of you to come.'

'I . . . ' Her voice stuck. She offered the flowers she had bought. 'I thought I should.'

Jane touched the furry yellow centres. 'Just like a bunch of sunshine. Thank you.'

She was older than Tara had expected. At least thirty, a touch of silver in the neatly tied back hair. And her face seemed oddly familiar. But then she remembered the photograph in the newspaper.

'Come and meet the son and heir.'

Almost numb, Tara moved around the bed. The baby was lying asleep in a small cot beside his mother, his fists bunched tightly against pink, downy cheeks.

'His hair is blond!' The words were startled from her. She had been so afraid he would be like Adam, with a mop of dark hair and green eyes. Stupid. All babies had blue eyes. He opened them and seemed to smile at her.

'Isn't it gorgeous.' Jane touched the soft curls. 'It will darken later, I suppose, but such fun.'

'He's beautiful.'

'Pick him up if you like.'

She lifted the tiny bundle into her arms and cradled him, touching the small fingers, letting them grip her own, comparatively huge one. She breathed the warm, milky smell of him and a wave of unbearable longing swept over her.

She glanced up to see Jane regarding her with great interest. 'You seem to have made a good recovery,' she said, quickly.

'Oh, yes. Just as long as I don't cough. It's hell on the stitches.'

Tara had thought it would be easy to hate Jane Townsend, but it wasn't. She was so natural, so easy to be with. 'Tell me about Bahrain. Did you enjoy yourself? How is Hanna?'

'He was very charming,' she said, tactfully.

Jane laughed. 'He kissed your hand and made you feel you were the most beautiful woman in the world?'

'He kissed my hand a lot.' But he couldn't make her feel beautiful because she had known it was just an act. 'I thought it was simply to annoy Adam.'

'Did it?' The question came so quickly that she immediately realised her mistake.

Conscious that Jane was watching her closely, Tara forced a smile to her lips. 'Of course not. Why should it?'

Jane's eyes narrowed slightly. 'Forgive me for being personal, Tara, but do you always dress like that?'

Tara glanced down at the monotone of her garments and remembered the red dress. 'Not always.'

'It's odd. Adam said you were a widow, but I had anticipated something merrier.' Tara started at the word but managed to keep the smile in place. 'He said you were beautiful, too, but I wouldn't have thought in the style that is constantly pursued by lusting men.'

He had clearly made her sound like some sort of Jezebel. 'I'm not,' she said, more sharply than she had intended. She forced the smile back into place. 'He just seems to catch me at my worst moments. He's been something of a Galahad.' Would she take this hint that his motives were totally pure?

'Yes. He would be. The sort of man any damsel in distress could trust with her life.' She glanced slyly at Tara. 'And anything else. If she wanted to trust him with it, that is.'

This was so unexpected that Tara had to look hurriedly back at the infant in her arms. 'Is he good? Charles Adam, I think you called him.'

'Yes, after his father and his uncle.' The door opened and she looked up. 'Speak of the devil and he's bound to appear. Hello, my darling.'

He stiffened in the doorway as he took in the sight of her sitting cradling the baby. 'Tara?'

'I asked her to come,' Jane said, a little defiantly, Tara thought. 'I wanted to meet her. I hope you've brought enough grapes for three.'

'No.' Tara rose to her feet and placed the baby gently in his crib. 'I must go.'

'Nonsense,' Jane said. 'Sit down, Tara. Adam won't stay long and he'll take you home if I ask him nicely. Won't you, darling?' Adam scowled at her.

'Of course.' He was curt to the point of rudeness.

She sat through agonies of embarrassment as he bent and dropped a careless kiss on the dark head of the woman in the bed. 'How are you today?' His voice softened for her.

'Desperate to go home. I hate this place.'

'Next week,' he said, firmly. 'And the little tadpole?' He leaned across and touched the baby's cheek. 'Hello, Charlie.'

'Don't call him that! His name is Charles!' To Tara's horror, Jane's face suddenly crumpled. 'Oh, Adam, I'm sorry, I just wish . . .'

'Sssh. It won't be long.' He sat on the bed and gathered her into his arms to comfort her. 'It won't be long now, I promise.'

Tara muttered an excuse and almost ran from the room. He caught her a hundred yards down the road. 'Where do you think you're going?' he demanded, turning her back towards the car park. 'I said I'd take you home.'

'There's no need. I need some fresh air. Hospitals make me feel queasy.' At least this one did.

'Really?' He gave her a hard look. 'Or

was it just a ploy to get me to chase after you?'

'Why on earth should I do that?'

'I have no idea.' He opened the car door for her and she got in quickly before he could touch her. 'Just as I have no idea why you came here today.'

'Jane telephoned and asked me to come and see her.'

'Why?' He was relentless.

'You'd better ask her.'

But she had been wrong about Jane's motive. She hadn't asked her to come to warn her off her man. She had simply wanted to demonstrate to her rival that she had no chance. She had wanted Tara to sit and hold the child that she and Adam had made, touch it, see how closely Adam was bound to her. She must have known that Adam would be visiting her this afternoon and had specified just the right time for Tara to call.

When the stage was set and all the players had been allocated their parts, she had produced the tears, turning the agony-screw, forcing her to witness Adam holding her, comforting her. Then she had thrown in the final humiliation, the consolation prize of a lift home. And Adam had accused *her* of being a good actress.

8

'Jane sends her apologies for the tears.' Adam glanced across at her as they waited at the exit to the car park for a gap in the traffic. 'Apparently it's quite common. The hormones go all to pieces.'

'You're quite the expert.' Her voice was scratchy and she hated herself for it. She had lost her heart, the least she could do was hang on to her self-respect. He must never know how much she was hurting.

'Hardly that,' he said as he pulled out, neatly avoiding a cab that cut across him.

The journey continued for some time in silence, each of them deep in their thoughts. Tara closed her eyes in an effort to blot out the overpowering presence of the man she loved, edgily aware of the precarious nature of her self-control. But the faint scent of some citrus-based cologne mingled with the leather of the upholstery and something wholly insubstantial that called to her, focusing every nerve-ending, until she gave up the unequal struggle and turned to look at him.

She had thought, in the first second she had seen him, that he was ruthless. And it was true, there was a drive, a dynamism that had carried him to a position of power and influence which he enjoyed without apology. But there was so much more. She had thought of him as a black knight, but that wasn't right. He had his faults, heaven knew, but he was on the side of the angels. He might even now regret his affair with Jane. The way he had kissed her that last day in his office had been more than simple lust. He had wanted her as much as she wanted him, and only her fingertip grasp on sanity had stopped them from making the most terrible mistake. But he was aware of his responsibilities to Jane and the baby and he would never desert her. That was right and she accepted it.

He turned suddenly and caught her staring. 'You sent the pearls back.' The unexpectedness of this statement, so far from her own thoughts, came as a shock. 'Why?' he demanded.

'What did you expect?' she asked. 'You refused to do it for me.'

'I thought you were being unnecessarily noble. Hanna could afford to be generous.'

'That's not the point.'

He glanced across at her again. 'You've quite shaken Hanna's faith in the avarice of women, you know.'

'You've spoken to him?'

'He telephoned in something of a panic, demanding to know what you wanted from him. What it would take to buy your silence. He assumed, you see, that returning the earrings was a very sophisticated form of blackmail. A suggestion that it wasn't quite enough.'

Her eyes widened in horror. 'No, Adam!' He had to believe her.

'I finally convinced him that if you had said you had forgiven him he could forget the whole thing. He's a broken man, Tara. He's not used to forgiveness without having to pay for his misdeeds. His wife extracts jewels like a quack dentist.' He half smiled. 'No anaesthetic.'

She looked at her hands nervously pleating her skirt. She could cope with anything but that smile. 'I could never have worn them.'

'Well, you've done yourself no harm. He's a powerful friend and he feels a debt of honour.'

'A singularly inapt phrase, if I may say so.'

'What? Oh, yes, I suppose it is.' They were stationary in traffic and he drummed his fingers impatiently against the steering-wheel.

Tara felt herself beginning to crack. It had been a dreadful day and being forced into his company this way was the most subtle form of torture. Looking out of the window she realised they were near a station.

'Look, I'm sorry you were lumbered with me, Adam. There's a station over there, I'll make my own way home from here.' She moved to unfasten her seatbelt.

'Stay where you are, the traffic's about to move.'

'Well, could you just pull over and let me out?'

He stared at her. 'Is my company really so abhorrent to you?' The traffic began to move, but he stayed put and in seconds an angry chorus of horns began to sound behind them.

'Adam!'

'Answer me!'

She couldn't lie. 'You said you didn't want to see me again. Ever.'

'Which just goes to show how much I know,' he said, bitterly. He glanced in his mirror and raised a placating hand to those behind before moving off.

'Please, Adam,' she implored.

He ignored her, accelerating away as the traffic cleared in front of them and the station was left far behind. 'Surely it's not too much to ask for your company for a few miles? You don't have to talk to me if that's a problem.'

She didn't answer. There was no point now. Apparently satisfied that this was a positive response, he slipped a cassette into the tape deck and the strains of Tchaikovsky's Violin Concerto filled the car, thankfully putting an end to the verbal sparring.

Tara closed her eyes, allowing the music to lift her and carry her where it would. She didn't open them, even when they came to a halt, assuming that it was simply traffic lights until he cut the engine and the silence flooded back.

Dragged back to reality, she looked around her. They were parked alongside the river. 'Where are we?'

'Somewhere in Buckinghamshire,' he said, enigmatically. 'Does it matter? I just felt like a walk. I've hardly seen the light of day all week and I'd like to blow the cobwebs away.'

'Won't it be dark soon?' she protested.

'Not for an hour. We'll just take a gentle stroll down by the river. Nothing strenuous.' He offered his arm. For a moment she held back. But he had been forced to bring her in order to indulge Jane's need to control him, and it would be churlish to insist on being taken straight home when he clearly wanted some fresh air. Truth to tell, she could do with some herself.

She slipped her hand under his arm and allowed him to lead her down to the waterside. They walked for a while along the bank. It was peaceful. The river was running smooth and strong, trailing out the willows, and the coots and mallards were busy about the bank. The warm spring evening had tempted out quite a few people, but as the light began to fade they all seemed to be heading in one direction. Adam followed them and Tara found herself being led into the warm interior of an ancient inn. He ducked under a low beam and approached the bar.

He turned back to her. 'What would you like?' It was the normality of it all that was so bizarre. He seemed completely unaware of the oddity of their situation. Perhaps that was the best way. Keep up the pretence of normality.

'A dry sherry, please.'

He ordered her sherry and a tomato juice for himself and led the way to a small table in the corner. For a moment he said nothing, just looked at her as if trying to make a decision.

'What did you think of Jane? Did you like her?' The question had an odd ring to it, as if her answer was important to him. There was no likelihood of their ever being friends. She hoped never to have to meet the woman again.

Her hand trembled as she lifted the glass to her lips. 'Our acquaintance was very brief,' she hedged. Then with more determination. 'The talk was mostly about the baby.'

A muscle in his jaw tightened at this

reminder of his elevation to the ranks of fatherhood. 'You looked very beautiful with a baby in your arms, Tara.'

She felt the slow burn of colour rising to her cheeks. There was no mistaking the look in his eyes.

'I'm not in the market for babies, Adam. I have a career.'

He leaned forward, taking her hand in his and she was powerless to stop him. 'Are you so determined on it? A life alone with only a pampered lapdog to lavish your affection on in your old age? Your husband died, Tara, but the world didn't end. It was a long time ago and it's time you started living again. You should be loved, cherished. Let me — '

Not the end of the world? He would never know how near to the end of the world it was. To have misjudged him so completely . . . Her voice was hoarse, but her meaning was like crystal. 'I can't help you, Adam.'

He sat back as if slapped. 'Then it's true. You're still in love with him.'

'I will always love him. Is that so strange?' Not the way I loved you, she thought, but at least Nigel had never hurt her.

His eyes snapped contemptuously. 'Even when you begged me to love you?'

The desire to strike back, to cause him pain to match her own, was overwhelming. 'We all have our needs, Adam. You were simply replacing my chosen partner for the evening. You were the one who backed out.'

'You little bitch!'

'What's the matter, Adam?' She felt utterly reckless because nothing mattered any more. 'Surely you didn't think only men could enjoy themselves in bed without any emotional commitment?'

A vein was beating fiercely at his temple. 'No, Tara. But I was fool enough to hope . . . ' His smile was deadly. 'It doesn't matter.' He stood up, seizing her elbow and pulling her after him out into the darkness of the riverbank. When he stopped in darker shadows of an ancient willow, he turned quickly and dragged her into his arms. 'If it's simply fun you want, Tara, I'm as game as the next man.'

'No!' She pushed violently at his chest with her hands, but he had expected that and was unmoved. He pulled her closer, fitting the curves of her body to his, letting her feel his arousal. Tara began to tremble. She had goaded him beyond endurance and now he was going to take her, here on the cold, damp grass in the darkness beside the river. Tears began to flow unchecked down her cheeks. After everything, it was finally to happen in a fit of anger. 'Please, don't.' Her voice broke on a sob.

He raised his hand to her cheek and felt the wetness. 'Tears?' He swore then and tore away from her. 'My God, Tara, you drive me to the edge of insanity. I want you so much that sometimes I think I hate you.' His breath was coming in short gasps. 'Don't you feel it? This . . . electricity.'

He grabbed her arm as if to shake an answer from her, but she flinched away and he stepped back, holding his hands high where she could see them, as if that would make her feel safe. 'Why do you deny it?'

'I need a little more than electricity to switch me on, Adam. I need someone who will love me all the time. Not just in the gaps between visiting Jane and her baby.'

'Jane? What on earth has she got to do with us?'

'Everything. That's why she wanted to see me today, Adam. She needed reassurance.'

'About what, precisely?' His voice jarred against her breastbone. He was angry now, but there was nothing she could do about that. Jane would have to deal with him herself. She seemed more than capable.

'You're the expert on hormones, Adam. She's just had a baby. She feels vulnerable. She wanted to be sure that I was no threat to her. I did my best and heaven knows, that's more than you deserve.'

His sudden harsh laughter was like a knife. 'Is that why you're dressed like a dowd?' She made no answer. 'It doesn't work, my lady. Don't you know that you would turn heads dressed in a sack?' Without warning he reached across and tugged the ribbon free from her hair, loosening it with his hands, his fingertips kindling hot trails of sensation, sparking the dangerous desire that raced through her bloodstream like vintage champagne.

'No!' She wrenched herself away and ran back into the inn, ignoring his bellow of rage at her escape.

The landlady took one look at her face when she asked to use the telephone and ushered her through to her sitting room to call a taxi, then left her tactfully alone to repair the damage to her tear-stained face, and brush out her hair.

She sat in the back of the cab as the miles flew past, trying not to think. But her mind seemed to have gone into overdrive and the only thing on it was Adam Blackmore. Vivid images flashed before her in an endless procession. His eyes as he launched an attack on an unwary opponent across the boardroom table; his eyes burning her up with desire. His hands firmly gripping a steering-wheel; his hand touching a baby's cheek; his hand against her skin.

'Is this it, miss?'

The driver's voice jerked her back to the reality, the pain of now. 'Oh, yes. Thanks. How much do I owe you?'

'The gentleman paid, miss.'

'Gentleman? But how did he know . . . ?' She saw the driver's expression alter to one of interest and stopped. It must have been obvious what she would do. Or maybe the landlady had told him. 'Can you tell me how much it was so that I can repay him?'

She passed Frank on her way into the mews reporting that all was well into his radio, and he raised his hand in greeting. She responded vaguely. Adam had apparently ignored her polite little note demanding his withdrawal. Well, he was hardly likely to worry about her safety after the dreadful things she had said to him this evening. Her face burned at the recollection. She had portrayed herself as the wanton he had believed her to be. Some wanton, who cried because the man she loved lusted after her. Her hand flew to her mouth and she ran for the bathroom.

* * *

It didn't take her long to pack. Her godmother was always too distracted with her own affairs to be over-interested in anyone else's. A week with her would clear the air, give her a breathing space to get herself under control.

She had telephoned Beth, who, sensing Tara's distress, but keeping any curiosity to herself, offered her car for the journey.

'It'll take forever on the train. And

don't worry about the office,' she forestalled her. 'I'll get someone in if I need help.' She paused. 'I take it you don't want your address given to anyone who might ask?'

'No one will ask.' She stopped overnight at a small hotel and telephoned Lally to warn her of her imminent arrival. Her complete lack of surprise was exactly what Tara needed. It would be a relief to spend a few days with someone who didn't know or care that Adam Blackmore existed.

★   ★   ★

She spent the days walking, reading, listening to music and watching Lally paint the delicate watercolours with which she illustrated her books on the world's flora. She had been her mother's best friend from her school-days, the only contact she had with the young unknown faces in old albums of photographs, and, when the mood took her, a fund of stories.

Lally had been in India on a field trip when Tara's parents were killed by a lorry plunging out of control across a motorway barrier. She had immediately returned to England to assume whatever responsibilities were to be thrust upon her, but Tara always suspected that it had been something of a relief to find her goddaughter already happily settled with the kindly neighbour who had been babysitting her while her parents went away for the weekend.

But she had dealt with the financial side of things and invested her parents' small estate so there was enough money for Tara never to be a burden to the Lamberts. Enough even for a deposit on the tiny new house she and Nigel were to have lived in.

She had always kept an eye on her from a distance. Always remembered the important things. And she had been there when she had been desperately needed. It was Lally who had taken the brunt of her grief when Nigel had died.

The week passed too quickly. She

arrived back at Beth's just before lunchtime on Sunday morning and her partner was delighted to see her.

'You're looking better.'

'I'm recovering, Beth. Apparently a broken heart isn't fatal.'

'Thank God for that,' she said with conviction. 'But it is like being ill. Take one day at time. You'll wake up one morning and realise that the pain isn't unbearable any more.'

'I'll take your word for it,' Tara replied.

'You've been there often enough.' Beth's eyes sparkled. 'I don't believe it! Not again?'

'This time it's the real thing. I swear it.'

Tara shook her head, wondering at her friend's stamina. Once was enough for her. 'And you were wrong about there being no enquiries for you.'

Her hand trembled and she set down the mug of coffee, afraid it might spill. She wasn't strong enough yet. 'He telephoned?'

'He came to the office.' Beth pursed

her lips. 'I know you think he's the pits, but frankly I was very taken with your Mr Blackmore.'

'He's not mine.' Her pulse was hammering in her ears. 'What did you tell him?'

'Simply that you had gone away and I wasn't at liberty to tell him where you were.'

'Did he just take that?' Why had she said that? Why did she want the answer to be no? She closed her eyes. It mustn't matter so much. Recovery was still a long way from certain.

'He didn't actually try to beat your address out of me, if that's what you're wondering.'

Tara flushed. 'Well, thanks.'

'You could be more enthusiastic. Did you expect me to crack under his charm and spill the beans? He looked fit to come after you.'

'Of course not,' she said, quickly.

Beth did not look convinced. 'Can I offer you something to eat?'

'No, if I can just beg a lift home via

the Italian shop to pick up some bread and milk.'

They had to drive by Victoria House to get to the mews. Tara kept her eyes firmly on the road ahead, terrified that he might just glance down from his penthouse and spot her. Beth said nothing, but Tara saw her mouth twitch.

'I know he can't see me. Doesn't even know your car. I just feel . . . vulnerable.'

She felt safer inside her flat. She stepped over the pile of mail and newspapers on the mat. It was home, a bolt hole, it represented safety. She checked the rooms. Everything was exactly as she had left it, apart from a week's dust that had settled quietly over the furniture. She whisked quickly around with the duster, then made herself a sandwich.

She forced herself to eat it. Every mouthful. If she kept going through the motions it might eventually become habit-forming. She washed the dishes, unpacked, loaded the washing machine, made her bed, vacuumed. Opened the mail and sorted it all to deal with at the office on Monday. All tedious little jobs that kept her mind from dwelling on heartache. But it was still only five o'clock.

A sudden desperation overtook her to stay busy. She would make Beth a chocolate cake. A thank you for loaning her the car. She switched on the radio to some cheerful commercial station and gathered her ingredients. The electric mixer was noisily whisking sugar and butter to soft peaks of cream to the accompaniment of the top twenty, when another sound, an insistent tapping, gradually began to overlay the general clatter. Tara switched off the whisk. It was someone knocking at the door.

Her first reaction was to switch the mixer back on and ignore it. She didn't want to see anyone and if it was next door she could always say she hadn't heard.

Tara sighed and turned down the radio. She wasn't much good at fibs. The only lie she had ever told with any conviction, the only one anyone had ever believed was the one she had told Adam about wanting Hanna Rashid.

Having decided to answer the door, she almost ran. There was no way of knowing how much longer her caller would wait.

But when she flung open the door she wished she had obeyed her first instincts. Her visitor was the last person in the world she expected to see. And the least welcome.

'Hello, Tara.' Tara took an involuntary step back. Jane Townsend, reading this as an invitation to enter, sailed blithely over the threshold. 'I'm so glad you're home. I was just about to give up and go away,' she said. 'May I use your bathroom? I'm afraid Charlie needs changing.'

9

Stunned as she was by the unexpectedness of Jane's arrival, Tara could do
nothing but direct her unwanted guest
to her bedroom with its tiny en-suite
bathroom.

Jane looked appreciatively around
her. 'What a lovely apartment. Adam
described it to me.' She glanced
sideways at Tara. 'Not the bedroom, of
course.'

Tara felt the swift rush of blood to
her cheeks and was furious with herself.
'Of course not,' she said, quickly. 'He
hasn't seen it.'

Jane laughed. 'That's what he said,
but I hardly believed him.' Seeing Tara's
shocked expression, she was immediately apologetic. 'I'm sorry, I shouldn't
tease. In fact, considering the state he's
in, it has to be the truth.' She held out
the baby. 'Could you take him while I

fetch his bag from the car?'

Tara took Charles Adam Townsend in her arms. He lay there, quite content, staring with unfocused intensity at her. He wasn't like Adam at all, she thought, or even much like Jane. It was probably the crop of fair hair, already growing fast and beginning to curl. She touched it and the baby grabbed for her hand, catching her little finger and pulling it down to his mouth.

It was a moment before she realised she was not alone. She looked up to find Jane watching her and she felt quite naked, as if she had exposed herself in some very private way.

'He likes you. He won't let just anyone hold him like that.'

Tara made an effort at a smile. 'Then I'm flattered.'

Jane retrieved her son and went about the task of changing him. 'That's better, isn't it, my darling.' She picked him up and kissed him. 'Much nicer.'

Tara led the way back to the living room and her unexpected guests settled themselves on the sofa, Charles accepting a small drink of water from a feeder.

'He's grown,' she said, and felt quite stupid at saying something so obvious. But she began to understand why mothers talked incessantly about their babies. Charles seemed to dominate the room with his tiny presence. But his mother had something else on her mind.

'How are you, Tara? I've been trying to phone you all week. We never had a chance to talk with Adam turning up when he wasn't wanted.'

'I've been away for a few days. It's been hectic at work and I needed a break.'

'Adam asked me to look in as soon as you got back, explain everything, make sure you were all right. He had to go to Wales, something to do with the new factory, I think, and since he didn't know when to expect you back there was no point in putting it off.' She looked up at Tara. 'Beth wouldn't tell him where you had gone.'

'I asked her not to.' A headache was beginning to tighten in a band around her forehead and she just wished Jane would go. For a while the only sound was that of the infant sucking.

'He looks terrible.' Tara made no comment. She told herself she didn't want to know why he looked terrible, but her eyes betrayed her and Jane went on. 'I don't think he's ever been in love before, and thirty-three is a bit late to taste the agony of it for the first time. If he wasn't suffering quite so much I have to confess that I would find it amusing.' She offered a tentative smile. 'Couldn't you be just a little kinder?'

'Kinder?' Tara stood up, folding her arms tightly about her chest as if she could hold in the pain. 'I don't understand you, Jane. Don't you love him?'

'Adam?' Jane frowned. 'Of course I love him.' She pulled a face. 'Although whether he feels the same way about me at the moment is in some doubt. According to the wretched man I'm as expensive and time-consuming as a wife, but none of the fun.'

'But that's . . . dreadful.'

Jane seemed quite unconcerned. 'He's got a point. I'm afraid I've exploited him quite shamefully.' Charlie grumbled for attention and Jane put him over her shoulder and patted his back gently. He promptly threw up. 'Oh, my poor darling. I'll take you home.' She groaned as she moved, her shirt sticking cold and wet to her back. Tara ran to get a towel from the bathroom and mopped up the worst of the damage. 'There wasn't much, but it seems to have gone rather a long way.'

'I'm sorry,' Jane apologised. 'One day perhaps we can talk for more than five minutes without interruption.' She stood up and gathered her belongings. 'I must get home and change Charlie.' She wrinkled her nose. 'And me. I'll phone you.'

Tara helped Jane down the steps with her bag, handing it over to the chauffeur of her silver Mercedes. Then she bolted for cover.

The wild surge of emotion that swept over her as she leaned weakly against her front door was not pleasant. Anger at herself and at him. Fury at fate for conspiring with such glee to show her love, only to snatch it from her lips. Rage against a life that determined she should be on her own for ever.

No. Not on her own. She flung herself across the room to the local paper, searching almost frantically through the pages for the for sale column. Pets. Retrievers, kittens, tropical fish. No lap-dogs. Not even a pug. She began to cry, hot bitter tears that seemed never-ending.

Afterwards she washed her hair, spent a long time in the bath, painted her finger and toenails a vivid defiant red, then wiped the polish off again, hating it. There was a comedy on the television. She switched it on and made a pretence of watching it. It made no sense to her, but another half-hour had gone by. She wondered, idly, how she had spent her time before she'd met

Adam Blackmore. There had never seemed enough hours in the day; now every hour seemed like a week.

Slowly she prepared for bed, pulling on the first thing that came to hand, an old nightdress, white with tiny pink flowers, a ruffle of lace at the throat and at the wrists, a deep frill to her toes at the hem. She brushed her hair until it hung in a shining ebony curtain. She would have it cut a little shorter, she decided, into one of those sleek bobs she had seen in a magazine. She had had enough of hairpins. She would make an appointment first thing in the morning.

And with that decision a determination to spring-clean her life overtook her. She opened her wardrobe and began to drag out all the dull, boring clothes she wore to the office. She carried them into the kitchen and bundled them into a plastic sack. They could go to the charity shop in the morning. Never, she fervently avowed, would she wear grey again.

Then, as she wondered what to do next, tiredness suddenly overwhelmed her, a combination of her long drive and an excess of emotion. She checked the door and windows and settled herself in bed. Ten minutes later she was fast asleep.

★   ★   ★

Someone was pounding on a stake with a mallet and she wished they would stop. It was a long way off, but the noise dragged her relentlessly back to consciousness. For a long moment, on the brink between sleep and waking, she thought she was dreaming. Then she sat up with a start. It was someone hammering at her door.

She switched on the lamp and looked at her alarm clock. It was nearly two o'clock in the morning. Someone must need help. She threw off the bedclothes, dragged on a dressing gown and ran to the door where a sudden attack of self-preservation made her slide the chain across before she opened it a crack.

'Tara, let me in!' He slammed the door back against the chain.

She fell back. 'Go away, Adam. I don't want to see you.'

He didn't bother to argue with her; he simply put his shoulder to the door and the wood splintered, the screws hanging on for a desperate moment before giving up the unequal struggle. The door burst open with a crash and Adam was standing in the opening, dark, angry, a day's growth of beard on his face. Then he stepped into her tiny hall, filling it, overwhelming her with his presence, and kicked the door shut behind him, without ever taking his eyes from her.

'Where the hell have you been?' he demanded.

She wanted to run, but her legs wouldn't obey her. Defiance was all that was left and she lifted her chin and hurled it at him. 'It's none of your business.'

'Wrong, Tara. I'm making it my business.' He moved swiftly and she backed nervously until the sofa was behind her knees and she had to stop or fall backwards across it. 'Who were you with?'

She closed her eyes to blot out the cold green fire in his eyes. 'Stop it, Adam. For pity's sake stop it,' she begged. 'Haven't you made me suffer enough?'

'Suffer? You, my lady? I don't believe you know the meaning of the word. You're ice all through. But I intend to make you suffer for the agony you've put me through this week.'

'You can't — '

'Believe it. You have my personal guarantee. You like to play games, Tara, lead a man on with those eyes that promise so much, until he's half mad, crazy with — '

She flung her head from side to side. 'You don't know what you're talking about.'

He grasped her shoulders, dragging

her towards him until she could feel the heat of his body, hammering in waves against her own. 'Oh, believe me, Tara, I know.'

She put her hands over her ears. 'Stop it! Stop it, do you hear? You've no right to say such things — '

'Then tell me. Who were you with?' His eyes were angry slits. 'The truth!' He shook her, fiercely. 'I promise you, I'll find out if you're lying.'

Her mouth was dry. She recognised in Adam a man at the end of his tether and saw the danger of goading him any further. Whatever he might believe, she had no intention of lying to him.

'I stayed with my godmother in Kendal for the week.'

'Your godmother?' This was clearly the last thing he had expected. He released her and she staggered slightly, retaining her feet with difficulty.

'I had to get away. I needed a breathing space. Some time — '

He raked his hand through his hair. The slash of silver across his forehead seemed more prominent than she remembered. 'Time.' He laughed bitterly. 'I've tried that. It doesn't work, does it?'

She shook her head. 'No. I'm afraid not. But there's nothing either of us can do about it.'

'Oh, yes, there is.' He groaned and pulled her roughly against him. 'Only one thing. Marry me, Tara. Put us both out of this misery.'

Shocked, she stood rigid, unresponding in his arms. 'How can you ask me that?'

'I'm simply bowing to the inevitable. I'm asking you to do the same. I know you still feel strongly for that boy who died, but you can't live your life in the past, Tara.'

'And Jane?' she asked, coldly. 'Is she to be relegated to the past as well?'

'Jane?' He stared at her. 'What has she to do with this?'

'She needs you, Adam. Her baby needs you.'

'For God's sake, Tara, haven't I done

enough? I can't give up a life of my own simply because her husband spends half of his life in one remote jungle after another — '

'Jungle?' Tara interjected.

'That's why she came to work for me, because she couldn't stand being in the house all day by herself.'

'And all night?' Tara demanded.

'All night? What are you talking about?' He held her at arm's length. 'My God, she didn't tell you!'

'Tell me what?'

'Didn't she come here? I made her promise that she would.'

So that was why she had come. To please Adam. 'You needn't worry. She kept her promise. She asked me to be . . . kinder.'

'But she never told you?'

'Told me what, Adam? What was so important?'

'I don't believe she could be so stupid. This baby has turned her wits to sawdust.' He stepped forward and took her shoulders and held her at arm's length. 'Jane phoned me in Wales to say you were home. I told her I was coming straight back and that she had better get around here and clear up all misunderstandings before I arrived.'

Her eyes were huge in her pale face. 'What possible misunderstanding could there be, Adam? Everything seems very simple.'

'No, my lady. The only simple thing around here is me, for allowing my sister to get me into a situation where I was in danger of losing the one woman I have found it impossible to live without. No matter how hard I tried.'

He watched while the words sank into her brain. 'Your sister?'

'Jane is my sister,' he repeated carefully, making sure she understood. 'She is married to Charles Townsend.' She didn't immediately respond to this information, still trying to take in what he was saying.

'Charles Townsend? The explorer?' She had seen photographs of him in a

Sunday supplement. A great blond Viking of a man.

'Yes,' he said, evidently relieved that he was finally getting through to her. 'By the time Jane realised she was pregnant it was too late for him to back out of this latest expedition. But I'm happy to assure you that young Charles is their sole property.'

She shook her head. 'But you were paying the bills for the clinic. You raced back from Bahrain . . . ' She stopped, a tiny bud of hope growing somewhere deep inside. She mustn't look at it too closely, or it would wither. 'Is this true?'

'He's been in the Amazon basin, Tara. Not exactly at the end of a telephone. He needed someone to rely on, someone to look after Jane while he was away, so I was lumbered with all the messy details. And the bills until Charles got home. I assumed you knew, I don't know why, but it just never crossed my mind to doubt it.'

'But why was she working for you?'

'She never could bear rattling around

the house all day when Charles was away. It worked very well.' He grinned. 'If I was unbearable she felt quite at liberty to be unbearable back.' He pulled her closer, holding her against him. 'Shall we sit down? That sofa looks comfortable and there are a few details to be worked out.' He tilted her chin up and kissed her, very gently. 'It may take some time.' She felt ridiculously shy as he looped his arm around her waist and pulled her down on to the sofa with him, drawing her so close that it was a struggle to breathe. 'Now,' he murmured. 'Where shall we begin?'

Tara turned in his arms and tentatively reached up to touch his face, letting her fingers gently trace the hard outline of his cheekbones, his jaw, his throat. He sat perfectly still, not rushing her, seeming to know that she needed time to get used to the idea that he was truly hers.

He caught his breath as she kissed him. Soft, gentle touches of her lips, hardly more than the caress of a butterfly's wing, at first. Then with more urgency, until all the suppressed longings of the past weeks exploded and she wrapped her arms around his neck, drawing him down to her, offering herself in complete and utter surrender.

When at last she released him, he smiled very slowly. First his mouth, then his cheeks, finally those fierce, compelling eyes creased.

'Those weren't quite the details I had in mind, my darling, but I guess they can wait.'

She laughed, delightedly, as he shrugged free of his soft leather jacket. Then his eyes smoked with a more urgent need and the laughter died away. As his lips brushed hers, a murmur of desire broke from her and she felt his body shiver with the effort of holding himself in check. The tip of his tongue teased softly at her mouth, parting her lips, tormenting her with lightning forays but not allowing her an opportunity to respond, holding her back until she thought she would scream.

He laughed softly, understanding all too well the desire that quickened her pulse. 'Slowly, my darling. It's worth the wait.' His hand gently cupped her throat, tilting her chin up, brushing back the curtain of hair from her face. But when he kissed her again, there was a new fervour and still it was not enough. The fires that raced through her body were making new demands, urgent demands that only Adam could fulfil.

She pulled at his soft chambray shirt, allowing her hands the freedom to explore the smooth skin of his back, revelling in the heady sense of power as his muscles tensed under her touch. Spurred on by his response, she grew bolder, stroking up the hard muscles of his stomach and across his chest until he gasped.

'You black-haired witch,' he murmured, his voice lost somewhere in his throat. 'You're driving me crazy.'

She lay back then, stretching her

arms above her head, offering herself to him.

He eased off her dressing-gown and groaned. 'What are you, Tara? You behave like a witch and look like a virgin.'

'Why don't you find out what I am for yourself?' she offered. He needed no second invitation, but swept her up into his arms and carried her through to the bedroom.

* * *

It was a long time later when he murmured into her shoulder, his voice hoarse with disbelief. 'You were both.' He eased himself away from her and for a moment she felt forlorn. Then his arm gathered her in and he pulled the quilt over them both and she nestled against his body. He stroked her hair, her face, lifting her lips once more to his. His smile was slow and content. 'I'm not complaining, you understand. But I hardly expected . . .'

'A virgin?' She shook her head. 'I never slept with Nigel. It didn't seem right at home. I'd have died of embarrassment if Aunt Jenny had found out.'

'Home? I don't understand.'

She lay in his arms and tried to think how to start to explain her life. At the beginning. With her birth. Her mother had suffered dreadfully from depression afterwards, she had been told, but she was recovering slowly. Jenny Lambert was a neighbour and friend and she suggested to her father they go away for a weekend, have a break. She would look after the baby.

They had never returned and she had never left the Lambert's house. Whether from a misplaced sense of guilt, or just a good heart, Jenny had taken on the responsibility of bringing her up alongside her own child.

'She adopted you?' Adam asked.

Tara shook her head. 'No. She was always just Aunt Jenny.'

'But then why is your name Lambert?'

'She had a son. Nigel. We grew up together. I'd always loved him, I suppose, like a big brother. But more than that. He was always protective. Always kind. Not like real brothers.' The memory was warm now. No pain. 'When he was eighteen he went away to art college. Each time he went back it was harder. I missed him so much. Then one day he phoned and asked me to go up to a college dance. I just thought he hadn't got another girl to go with, but I didn't care, I was over the moon. It was my dream come true. And apparently his too. As soon as he came home he asked me to marry him.'

Adam shifted slightly at her side and frowned. 'Didn't people think it a bit odd?'

'Why should they? Everyone knew that we weren't brother and sister. Aunt Jenny was delighted.'

'So what happened, Tara?'

She took a deep breath. 'He was specialising in jewellery design by then and he had been making a wedding present for me, a brooch — '

'Is that the one you wear all the time? Like a little lopsided V.

'Yes. It's my name in a shorthand outline,' she explained. 'I always signed my name like that when I wrote to him. I know it was silly — '

He stopped the words with his finger to her lips. 'No, not silly.'

'It had taken longer to finish than he thought. It was the tiny diamonds for the vowels that caused the problem and he wanted it to be perfect.' She hesitated, not sure if she could go on. He didn't press her, waited patiently until she was in control once more, stroking her hair, reassuring her. 'But he had to be home for the wedding rehearsal, Aunt Jenny had made such a fuss that everything should be perfect, and he was driving much too fast because he was late. He came off his motorbike and broke his leg.'

'So why didn't you cancel the wedding?'

'Aunt Jenny and Lamby were going

to New Zealand for six months. They had family out there and they had already put off the visit until after the wedding.'

'Well, that explains the very strange wedding photograph.'

'It was all good fun. We popped a bottle of champagne and the nurses joined in, then his parents went off to the airport and in the evening I went home. An odd sort of wedding night all on my own.' She had never since been able to stand the sound of the telephone ringing in the night. It brought it back, like a recurring nightmare to haunt her. 'He collapsed in the night. They tried to revive him, but it was a thrombosis. No one had expected . . . he was young . . . fit . . . '

'Oh, God.' His arms tightened about her. 'I'm so sorry.'

'I went to the hospital — '

'Don't distress yourself. There's no need to go on.'

'I have to finish now. Tell you everything.' She blinked back the tears.

'He had been carrying a donor card, you see, and they wanted me to agree — '

'You were alone? There was no one with you?' His voice was fiercely angry. 'How could they do that?'

The horror of that night would never leave her. 'I don't suppose it was easy for them. And it seemed a way of keeping him alive, of making his life mean something. But Aunt Jenny . . . when they came back for the funeral . . . she wouldn't talk to me. She looked at me as if she hated me.' Adam gently brushed away tears that were flowing freely now. 'They went back to New Zealand afterwards and I've never seen them or heard from them since.'

10

Adam let her weep, holding her, cradling her. It was a long time before he spoke. 'The Lamberts — did you try to keep in touch with them?'

'I wrote to them. Four or five times. My letters were returned unopened.'

'I can't believe the cruelty of it.' His arm clasped her convulsively and suddenly his voice was tight with anger. 'You were just a child.'

'Not quite. Eighteen. Nigel was twenty-one. You mustn't blame them, Adam. They'd lost their son.'

'And then they threw away a daughter. My poor Tara, however did you cope?'

'I'm not sure. Hard work helped. I sold the little house we were going to live in and bought this place. It took a lot of my time to decorate, get exactly how I wanted it.'

'And there's never been anyone else?'

'Plenty of men were willing to comfort the grieving widow,' she said. 'But I don't think they had anything very permanent in mind.' That was when the body armour started. The severe dark clothes, a cool frosty look that kept the office Romeos at bay, until the habit of saying no had become a way of life.

'It's hard to believe.'

Telling him seemed to have lifted a burden from her and she found that she could smile. 'Well, there was Jim Matthews. He wanted to marry me, you know.'

'Oh?' There was a sudden fierceness to his voice. 'And were you tempted?'

'Not even remotely. But he was difficult to convince. He thought it was a wonderful idea to have a twenty-four-hour-a-day captive secretary. He found it difficult to understand my reluctance, but then once Jim gets something into his head he's difficult to shift.'

'I have some sympathy with the man.

I intend to marry you myself.' He kissed her to demonstrate just how serious he was. 'But I think you'll find he has something else on his mind these days.'

'Why?' She was suddenly suspicious. 'What have you done?'

'I have a contact in the States who publishes picture-book horror stories. Jim's over there now working out a deal for a dozen books.'

Tara laughed. 'That's why I haven't been able to get hold of him.'

'Why would you want to do that?' he demanded. 'I thought you wanted him out of your life.'

'I thought I'd have one more try at convincing him of that. But you've apparently done it for me. Is there anything you can't make money out of?'

'In this instance there was no money involved. It just seemed like a good way of getting rid of a rival.'

'He was never a rival.'

'Perhaps you'd like to prove that.'

* * *

Tara woke to an unfamiliar buzzing. She frowned, turned over and then she saw him through the open door of the bathroom. She lay for a moment savouring the pleasure of the sight and sound of Adam shaving. Then the razor stilled and he was there, a towel wrapped around his hips, smiling at her.

He paused for a moment in the doorway. 'Hello, sleepyhead.'

She had thought she would feel shy, but she didn't. She held out her arms to him and he moved swiftly across the room and kissed her. She tangled her arms around his neck and encouraged him wantonly. But a few minutes later he removed himself with reluctance.

'I hate to interrupt you, my darling, when you're so obviously enjoying yourself, but it's half-past nine. We should both be somewhere else.'

'What a pity you're so strong-willed,' she murmured, and stretched languor-ously.

'Tara!'

She laughed, delighted. 'I just wanted to be sure you weren't *that* strong-willed.'

She showered and dressed in a soft pink shirt-waister, leaving her hair loose about her shoulders. His eyebrows were expressive as she walked through into the kitchen and helped herself to the coffee he had made. She returned the compliment, raising her eyebrows at his dark business suit, fresh shirt and tie.

'Are you always so well prepared when you call on a lady in the middle of the night?' she asked, a teasing light dancing in her eyes.

'My bag was in the car. But I'm afraid I've scandalised your neighbours. I think every one of them must have put out their milk bottles in order to have a better look.'

Tara was unconcerned. 'You can hardly blame them after the racket you made last night.'

'Perhaps not.' He grinned. 'Shall I go round and apologise to them all?'

'Er — no. I don't think so. But you

could get Janice to send someone to repair my door. You do still have Janice?' she asked.

'Janice has been a lot harder to shift than the first two. But her job's quite safe now. I don't want you in the office. I have other plans for you.'

'Oh?'

'You might well say 'oh', my lady. I wasn't *that* well prepared last night, which is why I plan to marry you at the earliest possible moment.'

She lowered her lashes. 'Did you ask me to marry you, sir? I have no recollection of it.'

'That's odd. I distinctly recall mentioning it twice,' he replied. She sipped her coffee. 'Oh, I see. You want the whole bit. Down on one knee?' She kept her eyes averted, so that his sudden move took her by surprise and when her eyes flew open he was indeed upon one knee before her. He took her hand. 'Will you marry me, my lady? I'll love you and cherish you — '

'Adam, get up!' She laughed. 'I didn't

think you'd do it.'

'I only plan to do this once, Tara,' he swore, emphatically. 'So it might be a good idea to say yes with all possible speed, before I abandon you to a life of horror with Jim Matthews.' His eyes glinted wickedly. 'Maybe you'd prefer to have his slimy green monsters morning, noon and night.'

'No!' she said with a shudder.

'You're quite sure?'

'Positive.'

He stood up. 'In that case . . . ' he put his hand in his pocket and drew out a small jeweller's box ' . . . maybe this will help you make up your mind.' He opened it to reveal a solitaire diamond that the sun streaming in through the window lit with a thousand fires. He slipped it on her finger and kissed her hand.

'Adam, it's beautiful.'

'Can I take that as a yes?'

'You know it is.' He pulled her into his arms and for a long time neither of them said anything.

The urgent peal of the telephone finally parted them. 'It'll be Beth, wondering if I'm ever coming to work,' she said.

'Shall I answer it?' he offered.

'No!' She dived across the room and grabbed the phone and Adam bent to pick something from the carpet. It was a ribbon. A red ribbon.

He saw her puzzled expression. 'Every knight is entitled to carry his lady's colours, Tara. And yours are most definitely red.' He touched her flushed cheeks.

'Tara? Are you there?' Beth's voice said plaintively. But Tara didn't answer. She replaced the receiver without saying a word and went into his arms.

★ ★ ★

Beth said nothing when Tara arrived after lunch. She had seen her partner arrive in Adam's car and she sat with a smug, contented expression as if the whole thing had been her idea. One look at Tara's flushed and happy face had been enough to convince her that everything was right with the world. A second glance had taken in the ring and all the day's conversation had revolved around the coming wedding.

They had called at the register office on the way into their respective offices and confirmed that if they wished to be married by licence the wedding could take place as early as Wednesday.

Tara made no outward show of her disappointment when Adam suggested they needed a little longer to give them time to make all the arrangements. But a week on Friday hadn't felt quite like the 'earliest possible moment' that he had promised.

And he was distracted when he called at the office later that afternoon. Sensing he had more than dalliance on his mind, Beth withdrew on an errand to the bank to give them some privacy.

'I have to go away, Tara.' He raked back his hair. 'I'm not sure when I'll get back, but I'll be there for our wedding.'

There was a cold little spot of fear deep in her heart. She didn't want to let him out of her sight, terrified that something would go wrong, that fate would once more dash the cup of happiness from her lips.

'Where are you going?' she asked.

He leaned across the desk and kissed her mouth and she knew with absolute certainty that he had no intention of telling her. 'Janice is organising everything. Flowers, cars, reception. I'll see you a week on Friday.'

She sat behind her desk, her hands neatly folded in front of her, a picture of serenity, while inside she felt quite sick. 'I'll be waiting.'

His answering smile was all on the surface. She had seen him do that at meetings when underneath a thousand thoughts were churning away. Something had happened since this morning. Something he didn't want her to know about.

'Will you telephone me?' she asked, as he paused in the doorway, and recognised a certain desperation in her voice.

'I'll try, my darling. Now I must go, or I'll miss my plane.' He walked quickly back and kissed her again and as if he sensed her unease he drew her from her chair and held her. 'I love you, Tara. I'll always love you.' But apparently not enough to trust her.

If she had had the wedding arrangements to attend to it might have been different. She would have had something to occupy her mind in the long light spring evenings. But Janice had taken care of everything and Jane was holding the reception at her home.

Tara had been there, met her bearded explorer husband, but they hadn't volunteered any information on the whereabouts of the man she was about to marry. And she couldn't bring herself to ask. But one mystery had been cleared away: the newspaper photograph of Jane with the baby and Adam. It had been a story on the arrival of Charles Townsend's son while the famous man was hacking his way through the rainforests of South America. If she had only read it, she would have known then.

Adam phoned just once, sounding weary, talking apparently from the ends of the earth on a line that crackled and hissed and made anything but the commonplace courtesies impossible. Any whispered love words were swallowed up by static. Or perhaps he never murmured them.

★ ★ ★

'You look beautiful, Tara.' Jane made the slightest adjustment to the ivory curve of veil that swept from her hat. 'Quite perfect.'

'Thank you.' At Jane's insistence she and Lally had spent the seemingly endless night before her wedding with her future sister-in-law and her husband. Now it was time to go. She turned her head and saw her reflection in the long mirror. The simple silk dress, the tiny hat, the single red rose in her hand.

She sat pale and silent in the rear of the car, twisting the diamond around the third finger of her right hand, its temporary home until after the wedding. Last night she had been certain he would phone. But he hadn't. She had no idea if he was even back in the country. She was so certain that something had happened to him that the nerves stabbed through her like spears.

When they arrived at the register office the sudden quiet was enough to confirm her deepest fears. The arrival of the bride before the groom was not a good omen.

Everyone made a great effort to make a joke of it. Jane seemed unperturbed, but then her only concern at the moment was the welfare of her son and her husband.

'Mr Blackmore and Mrs Lambert?' The registrar looked around him expectantly.

Charles intervened. 'There's been a slight delay. I wonder if we could just wait — ' Everyone turned at the hurried sound of feet on the stairs.

'Hello. Am I late?' He kissed her cheek and took her hand. 'You weren't worried, were you? The traffic from Heathrow was murder.'

In his presence all the nameless horrors evaporated like the early morning mist on a hot June morning.

'Timed to a hair's breadth, I'd say,' Charles Townsend's voice boomed across the vestibule.

But Tara's eyes, for the moment riveted on Adam, were drawn slowly to the two people standing behind him.

Older, greyer, smaller than she remembered, but so familiar. She took a tentative step towards them. 'Aunt Jenny?' She took another step and then she was in the older woman's arms, hugging her. She turned to Lamby and he held her for a moment. 'I don't believe it.' The tears sprang to her eyes. 'I don't believe it.'

'Adam came and fetched us, Tara.'

She turned to him. 'You did that? For me?'

He smiled down at her. 'My wedding present.' The registrar cleared his throat. 'Although if we don't make a move right now I think this gentleman may make us wait a few more days.'

The party made a move, but Adam held her back. 'I'm sorry I couldn't tell you. I didn't want to raise your hopes. I didn't know if they would come.'

'Who could ever resist you?' She shook her head in wonder. 'Why did I ever think of you as a black knight?'

'I'm sure I gave you every reason, my love.'

'No. You've always been my true knight errant. Always there when I needed you.'

'I always will be, my lady.' He lifted the veil and stole a kiss. 'You have my promise.'

THE END

We do hope that you have enjoyed reading this large print book.

Did you know that all of our titles are available for purchase?

We publish a wide range of high quality large print books including:
Romances, Mysteries, Classics
General Fiction
Non Fiction and Westerns

Special interest titles available in large print are:
The Little Oxford Dictionary
Music Book, Song Book
Hymn Book, Service Book

Also available from us courtesy of Oxford University Press:
Young Readers' Dictionary
(large print edition)
Young Readers' Thesaurus
(large print edition)

For further information or a free brochure, please contact us at:
Ulverscroft Large Print Books Ltd.,
The Green, Bradgate Road, Anstey,
Leicester, LE7 7FU, England.
Tel: (00 44) **0116 236 4325**
Fax: (00 44) **0116 234 0205**

Other titles in the
Linford Romance Library:

THE WAYWARD HEART

Stella Kent

Francesca had loved her unruffled way of life, working in the Lynford bookshop with fatherly Mr. Pinkerton. But it had all come to an abrupt end when the shop was sold over Mr. Pinkerton's head, by his nephew Adam. The news caused the old man's death, and fury overwhelmed Francesca. But when Adam offered her a job in the Paris bookshop, she accepted. Here was a chance to get all she could out of a particularly heartless man . . .

A KISS AND A PROMISE

Moyra Tarling

Just as Autumn Daniels is getting her life back together after her husband's death, Matt Kingston returns. He'd left her five years ago with a kiss and a promise he never kept. Then, pregnant and alone, she'd turned to his brother — however, his proposal of marriage was just an elaborate scheme of vengeance. But now, as Matt melts the ice around her heart, is it Autumn he wants — or his daughter? This time, is his promise of love forever?

TOMORROW'S PROMISE

Gillian Villiers

Lara is determined never to risk falling in love, but when she takes up a new teaching post, finds it isn't quite so simple. She shares a house with fellow teacher Mick, whose laid-back manner hides a warm heart that threatens to melt even Lara's cool exterior. Trying to distract herself with a spot of property development only seems to involve her in endless problems, which Mick is more than happy to help resolve. But should she let him?

FOLLOW YOUR HEART

Margaret Mounsdon

Marie Stanford's life is turned upside down when she is asked to house sit for her mysterious Aunt Angela, who has purchased a converted barn property in the Cotswolds. Nothing is as it seems . . . Who is the mysterious Jed Soames and why is he so interested in Maynard's? And can she trust Pierre Dubois, Aunt Angela's stepson? Until Marie can find the answers to these questions she dare not let herself follow her heart.

A LOVE WORTH WAITING FOR

Karen Abbott

In the lovely village of Manorbier in Pembrokeshire, Jasmine gets the opportunity to open up a teashop — her dream come true. However, disturbing events threaten her business prospects, forcing Jasmine to search her heart and discover who wants the teashop closed. Is it the controlling boyfriend she has put in the past? Or someone wanting the premises for himself . . . local artist Rhys Morgan, for instance? Jasmine has to put her heart on hold until the sinister campaign is over.